The Classical Piano Method
Method Book 1

Hans-Günter Heumann

ED 13352D

www.schott-music.com

Mainz · London · Madrid · Paris · New York · Tokyo · Beijing
© 2012/2019 Schott Music GmbH & Co. KG, Mainz · Printed in Germany

About the author:

Hans-Günter Heumann is a freelance composer and author, living in southern Germany.

Since studying piano, composition, and music pedagogy at the Musikhochschule Hannover, followed by further studies in the USA, he has dedicated himself to the editing of pedagogical piano material. He has a particular interest in presenting music in an accessible way to reach a broad audience.

Based on many years of experience teaching children, young people and adults, Hans-Günter Heumann has written a great number of internationally successful and award winning publications, and has composed and arranged piano music in a range of styles for beginners to advanced students.

Having developed successful, methodical concepts for learning how to play the piano for all age groups and abilities, Hans-Günter Heumann's work has been translated into many different languages and sold millions of copies, an indication of the wide-spread appreciation of his work.
His publications *Klavierspielen – mein schönstes Hobby* and *Piano Kids* (both published by Schott Music) have become two of the most significant piano methods in the German language.

Acknowledgments

The author and publishers would like to thank Carol Klose and our colleagues at Hal Leonard Corporation for expert suggestions, support and advice in the development of *The Classical Piano Method*.

ED 13352D
British Library Cataloguing-in-Publication-Data.
A catalogue record for this book is available from the British Library.
ISMN 979-0-2201-3844-7
ISBN 978-1-84761-502-2

Cover design by www.adamhaystudio.com
Cover photography: iStockphoto
Layout and Engraving: www.bbruemmer.de
English translation: Wendy Lampa
Printed in Germany S&Co.8701

Contents

4 | Contents

Lesson 1

The Piano and its Precursors

clavichord

 The piano was invented in 1700 by the Italian musical instrument maker **Bartolomeo Cristofori (1655-1731)** in Florence. This was certainly one of the greatest inventions of the time. There is a plaque in the Basilica di Santa Croce in his memory.
Three well-known keyboard instruments may be regarded as its precursors: The **clavichord**, the **harpsichord** and the **spinet**.

harpsichord

On these instruments it was not possible to play gradually louder or quieter. This was only possible on the piano, with its small felt hammers striking the strings. The instrument was originally named Hammerklavier (hammer piano) to reflect this. A larger form of this piano is the grand piano.

Because of this, Cristofori called his invention **gravicembalo col piano e forte** meaning a large harpsichord which can be played both loudly and softly.

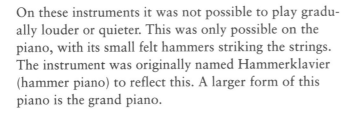
Cristofori's grand piano

spinet

From this the Italian term **pianoforte** or **fortepiano** was derived (Ital. piano = quiet, forte = loud). Today the term has been shortened to **piano**.

The term 'piano' is now often used as a collective term to refer to both upright and grand pianos. In an upright piano the strings are vertical, whereas in a grand piano the strings are horizontal.

grand piano

upright piano

How are Sounds Produced on the Piano?

When you press a key down, a small felt hammer inside the instrument hits a steel string and makes it sound. This produces a note. There is one hammer for every note on the keyboard.

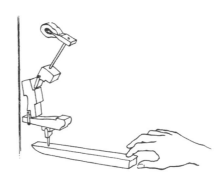

How to Sit at the Piano

Sit in an upright but relaxed position at the centre of the keyboard.

Sit towards the front edge of the stool, so that your feet are firmly on the ground. Your distance from the piano should be such that your hands comfortably reach the keys. The keys should be struck towards the edge, and the weight of your body should be supported by the spine rather than by your arms or legs. Sit close enough to the piano so that your knees are slightly beneath the instrument.

Your arms should remain relaxed and the shoulders should not be raised. There should be a space between your upper arms and the sides of your body.

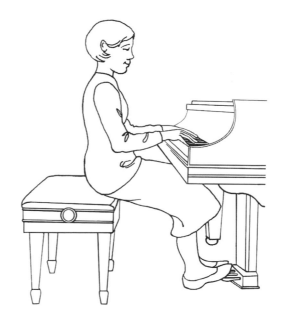

Hand and Finger Position

Your fingers should touch the keys so that the forearm, wrist and back of the hand form a straight line. The height of the piano stool should be adjusted accordingly.

Your fingers should be softly curved, as though you were holding a small ball in your hand.

Only your fingertips should touch the keys; the finger-nail should be at right-angles to the key.

Your thumb should be gently rounded.

Fingering

For playing the piano, each finger is given a number. These numbers appear above or below the notes, indicating which fingers to play the notes with. The figures are known as fingering and should always be followed precisely.

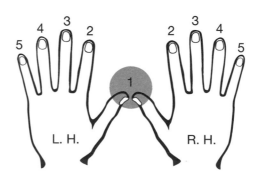

Lesson 2 —————————————

The Keyboard

All the keys on the piano together make up what is known as the **keyboard**. It consists of white and black notes. The piano keyboard usually has **88 keys**.

low – downwards ⬅ keyboard ➡ upwards – high

The Black Keys

The black keys are arranged in groups consisting of:

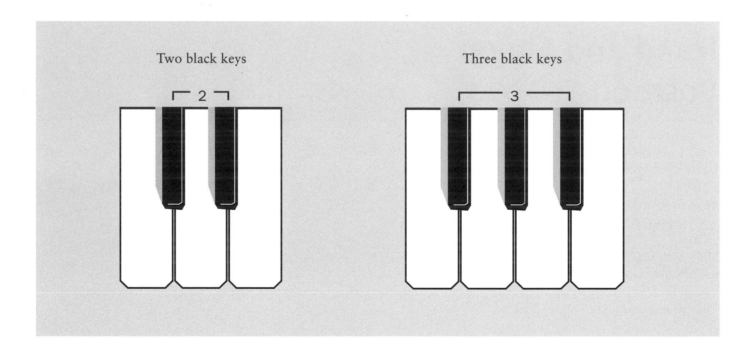

Two black keys

Three black keys

The Beat in Music

Music usually has a regular beat, similar to the beating of the heart. The beat or pulse can have different tempos – from very slow to very fast.

The following exercises and pieces should be played slowly at first with each note held for the same duration.

Two Black Keys

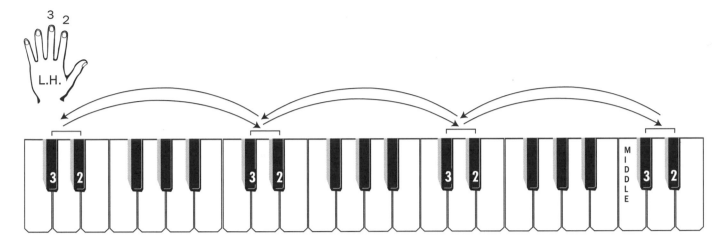

Playing Tips:

With the left hand, hereafter L.H. (fingering: 3 2), play four groups of two black notes, from the lowest pair to the middle (approximately in the middle of the piano), upwards and downwards. First play the pair of notes one after another, then together, and then alternating the two patterns.

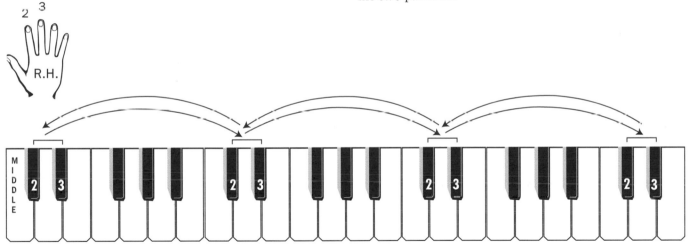

Playing Tips:

With the right hand, hereafter R.H. (fingering: 2 3), play four groups of two black notes, from the middle pair to the highest, upwards and downwards.

Play the pairs of notes one after another, then together, and then alternating the two patterns.

Technique Tips:

The change over from one finger to the next takes place at the lowest point at which the keys are depressed. This means that the finger leaves the bed of the key only when the next finger reaches it. This is the same as walking up the stairs – the transfer of weight from one leg to another happens only when the other foot reaches the ground.

First depress each key using the whole weight of your arm. When changing keys, the weight is transferred to the next finger.

At first play slowly, making sure that the fingers do not overlap. Make sure you maintain the correct hand and finger position.

Notation

Music can be written down or notated in print. These graphic symbols show the duration or 'value' of a note, that is, indicating for how long the note should be held.

Quarter Note / Crotchet

A quarter note lasts for one beat.

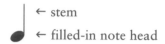

← stem

← filled-in note head

Count: 1
clap

TAKE TWO

Hans-Günter Heumann

Track 1/2

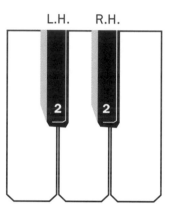

L.H.   R.H.

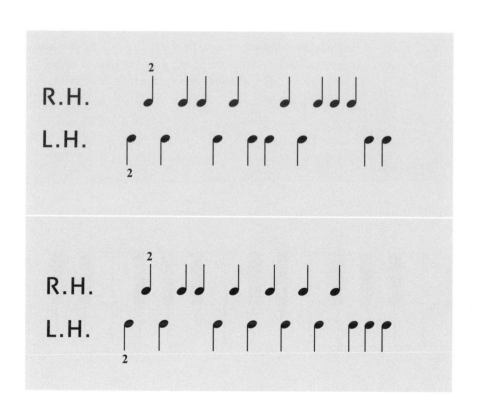

R.H.

L.H.

R.H.

L.H.

 Playing Tip:

Play the exercise with the groups of two black notes in the middle of the keyboard, using both hands alternately.

Accompaniment

When you are playing with an accompanist (teacher or friend), it will usually be necessary to play an octave higher to avoid collisions.

With the accompaniment, student begins here:

♩ = 80

Three Black Keys

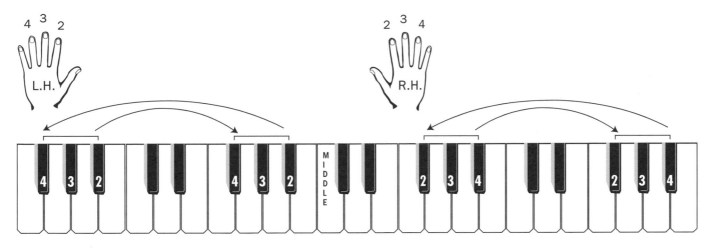

■ Playing Tips:

With the L. H. (fingering: 4 3 2), play two groups of three black keys, upwards, followed immediately by the R. H. (fingering: 2 3 4). Then continue immediately in the opposite direction – downwards. Pay attention to the hand position on the raised keys.
Again, the notes may be played one after another or together.

Improvising on the Black Keys

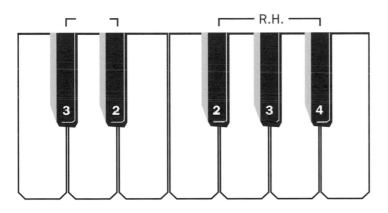

■ Playing Tips:

Improvise – that is make up – a beautiful melody to the accompaniment. Position your hands on the keyboard as shown in the diagram to the left.

The melody may go upwards or downwards. Repeated notes may also sound good.

Make sure you play the notes of the melody evenly.

Accompaniment   With accompaniment, student plays one octave higher than written.

Track 3

♩ = 80

mf

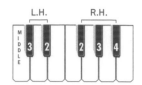

PIANO DREAMS

Keyboard Diagram   Hans-Günter Heumann

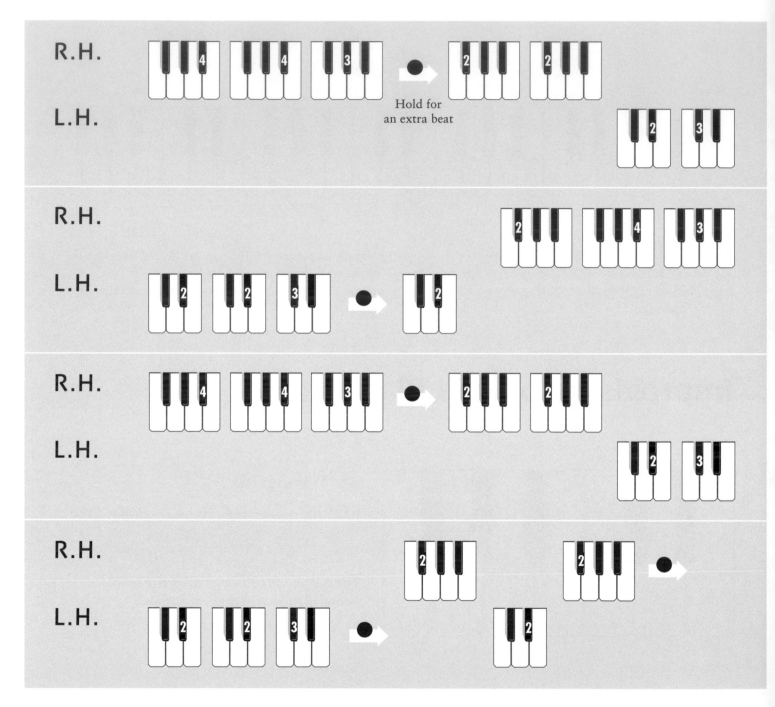

Hold for
an extra beat

Accompaniment   With accompaniment, student plays one octave higher than written.

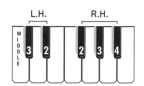

PIANO DREAMS

Notated

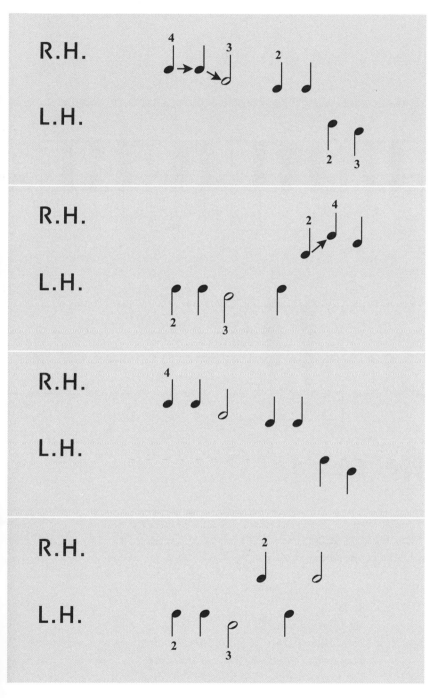

Half Note / Minim

← stem

← clear note head

A half note lasts for two beats.

Count: 1   2
        clap hold

Repetition →

Movement on the same key

Step ↗↘

Movement from one key to the next –
upwards or downwards

Skip ↗ ↘

Movement from one key to the next but one

Practice Tip:

Slow practice: Practice as slowly as you
need to play without mistakes or hesitation.
Then gradually increase the tempo.

Lesson 3

The White Keys - The Musical Alphabet

Musical pitches use the first seven letters of the alphabet: A B C D E F G

The letters of the musical alphabet are the names of the white keys. They are repeated along the piano keyboard.

Three White Keys

The black keys help you to find your way around the piano keyboard. They allow you to grasp the layout of the keyboard and to identify the white keys.

The group of three white keys around the group of two black keys is: C – D – E

Finding Three Notes with Eyes Closed

Playing Tip:

Close your eyes and find the two black notes by feeling the keys (L. H.: 3 2, R. H.: 2 3).
In this way you can find and identify the three white keys grouped around the two black keys.

L. H.:
1st finger = note E
2nd finger = note D (slide the 2nd finger from the black note to the left on to the white note)
3rd finger = note C (slide the 3rd finger from the black note to the left on to the white note)

R. H.:
1st finger = note C
2nd finger = note D (slide the 2nd finger from the black note to the right on to the white note)
3rd finger = note E (slide the 3rd finger from the black note to the right on to the white note)

Accompaniment: Black and White   With accompaniment, student plays one octave higher than written.

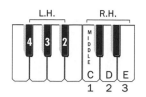

BLACK AND WHITE

Track 6/7

Hans-Günter Heumann

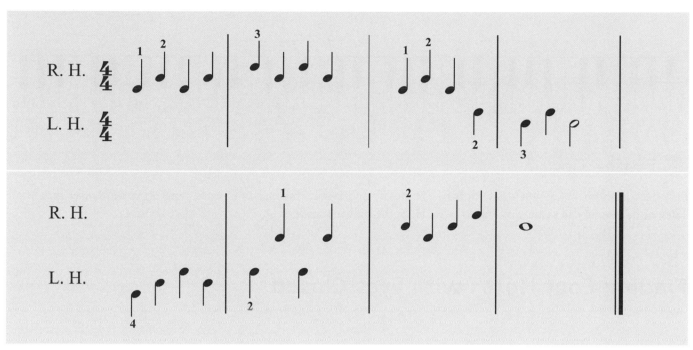

Measure / Bar, Bar Line

The bar contains a group of beats, e.g. four in a bar:

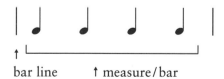

Bar lines separate the beats into bars.

bar line   ↑ measure / bar

4/4 Time

$\frac{4}{4}$ $\left(\frac{4}{4}\right)$ = 4 beats per bar
= The quarter note (crotchet) forms the beat.

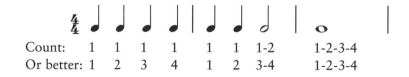

| Count: | 1 | 1 | 1 | 1 | 1 | 1 | 1-2 | 1-2-3-4 |
| Or better: | 1 | 2 | 3 | 4 | 1 | 2 | 3-4 | 1-2-3-4 |

Whole Note / Semibreve

𝅝   A whole note has a clear note head without a stem and lasts for four beats.

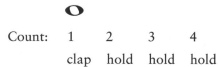

| Count: | 1 | 2 | 3 | 4 |
| | clap | hold | hold | hold |

Double Bar Line (End)

The end of a piece is indicated by a double bar line, consisting of a thin bar line followed by a thick one.

Four White Keys

The group of four white keys around the group of three black keys is:

F – G – A – B

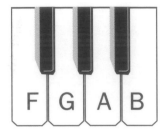

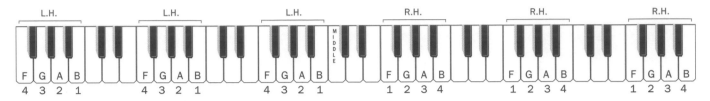

■ Playing Tip:

Play the four notes F – G – A – B with the L. H. slowly and evenly three times upwards and downwards (see diagram). Then continue, in the same way with the R. H. in the higher registers.

Finding Four Notes with Eyes Closed

■ Playing Tip:

Close your eyes and feel for the three black keys   (L. H.: 4 3 2, R. H.: 2 3 4).
In this way you can find and identify the four white notes grouped around the three black notes without looking.

L. H.:
1st finger = note B
2nd finger = note A (slide to the left with the 2nd finger from the black key on to the white key)
3rd finger = note G (slide to the left with the 3rd finger from the black key on to the white key)
4th finger = note F (slide to the left with the 4th finger from the black key on to the white key)

R. H.:
1st finger = note F
2nd finger = note G (slide to the right with the 2nd finger from the black key on to the white key)
3rd finger = note A (slide to the right with the 3rd finger from the black key on to the white key)
4th finger = note B (slide to the right with the 4th finger from the black key on to the white key)

Edvard Grieg
(1843-1907)

Country: Norway
Period: Romantic
(1820-1900)
Works: around 80

Grieg is one of the most important Norwegian composers. He researched Norwegian folk music and developed an un-mistakable national style. Above all, he was a master of small forms such as songs, piano pieces and chamber music works. Amongst his most famous pieces are: *Peer Gynt Suites* 1 and 2, *Lyric Pieces* for piano and the Piano Concerto in A minor.

MORNING IN THE COUNTRYSIDE

 Track 8/9

from *Peer Gynt Suite* No. 1, Op. 46

Edvard Grieg (1843-1907)
Arr.: Hans-Günter Heumann

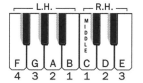

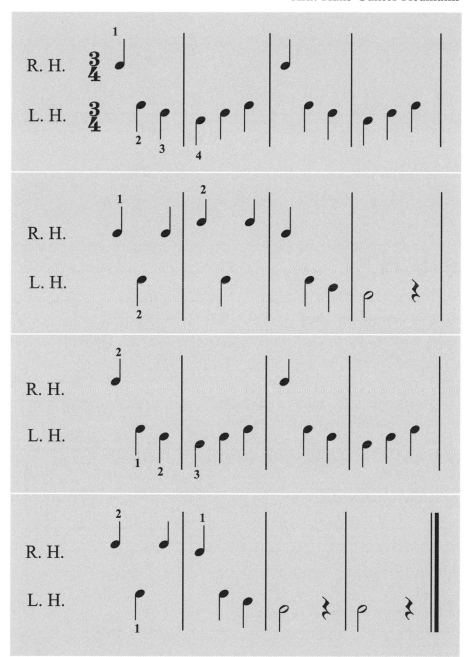

3/4 Time

$\frac{3}{4}$ $\left(\frac{3}{♩}\right)$

3 = 3 beats per bar

♩ = The quarter note (crotchet) forms the beat.

$\frac{3}{4}$ ♩ ♩ ♩ | ♩ ♩ | ♩ ♩

count: 1   1   1 | 1   2 | 1
or better: 1   2   3 | 1   2 | 3

Quarter Rest / Crotchet Rest

𝄽 Rest symbols represent a silence. A quarter rest lasts for one beat.

Opus, Op. = work, composition

▦ Technique Tip:

For a rest, release the weight of the arm, whilst resting the finger on the surface of the key.

Accompaniment
With accompaniment, student plays one octave higher than written.

♩. = 40

p

Lesson 4

The System of Stave Lines

⬤ Notes are written on **lines** or in **spaces**:

⬤ Music is written on a group of lines, consisting of
5 lines and 4 spaces, called a **stave** or **staff**:

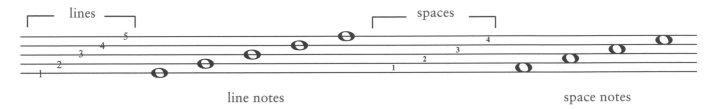

line notes   space notes

⬤ The placement of a note on the stave, combined with a clef, gives the exact pitch or name of a note.

Bass Clef for the L.H.

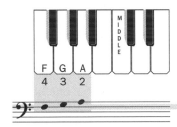

Notes in the bass clef are usually played with the left hand.

F line
The bass clef is also called the **F clef,** because it begins on the fourth line from
the bottom which also has two dots on either side of it.
The F line in the bass clef is an ideal reference point to help you identify the
notes, by working up or down either side of it.

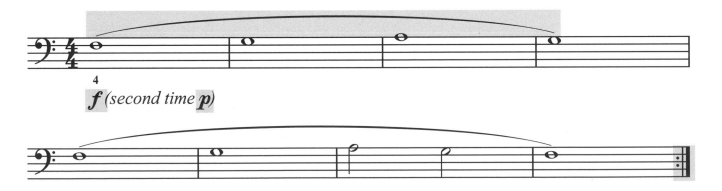

f (second time *p*)

Dynamics   The term **dynamics** means the different levels of volume in a composition. These differences
make music more expressive. Most dynamic markings appear in Italian and are usually given as abbreviations.

f **forte** = loud   *p* **piano** = soft

Legato	**Slurs**
Play smoothly, without gaps between the notes.	Play all the notes beneath or above legato.

Phrase
Curved lines, or phrase marks, are also used to group notes into musical sections or phrases.

Technique Tips:

To play a note loudly (forte), depress the key using the full weight of the arm.

To play a note quietly (piano), depress the key using just a little arm weight.

Move smoothly (legato) from one finger to the next. Play each phrase legato, beginning with a downward movement of the arm and ending with an upwards movement of the wrist.

Treble Clef for the R.H.

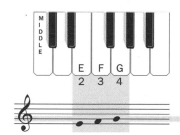

Notes in the treble clef are usually played with the right hand.

G line
The treble clef is also called the **G clef**, because it circles around the G line (2nd line from the bottom).
The G line in the treble clef is an ideal reference point to help you identify the notes, by working up or down, either side of it.

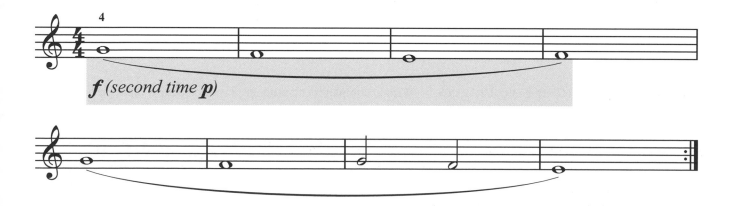

f (second time p)

The **repeat sign** is similar to the double bar-line at the end of a piece, preceded by two dots. It means: play again from the beginning.

Lesson 5

The Piano Notation System

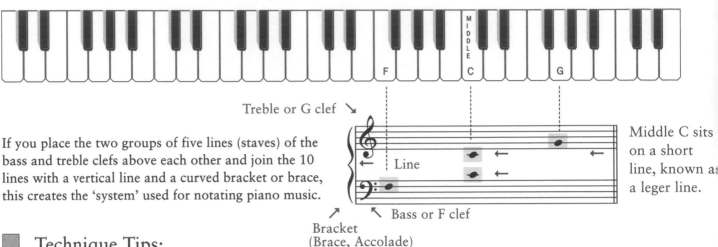

Treble or G clef ↘

Line

Bracket
(Brace, Accolade)

Bass or F clef ↖

Middle C sits
on a short
line, known as
a leger line.

If you place the two groups of five lines (staves) of the bass and treble clefs above each other and join the 10 lines with a vertical line and a curved bracket or brace, this creates the 'system' used for notating piano music.

◼ Technique Tips:

The piece *Take Five Fingers* uses a range of five notes in each hand. Each finger has its own key. The thumbs of each hand share the note Middle C.

When one finger depresses a key, the others remain in a relaxed position gently resting on or slightly above their keys. The hand and fingers should be free of tension and the fingers should remain curved.

Feeling the bed of the keys: Depress all five keys in this note range. Now play four repeated notes evenly with the first finger. On the fourth note, the finger remains on the key bed. Now the second finger follows, and so on.

◼ Practice Tips:

Sectional practice: You can learn more quickly if you practice in small sections or passages. The experience of

success is more quickly established, which can increase motivation and enjoyment.

Problem passages should always be practiced on their own, and repeated many times. After that, it is important to practice them in context.

The following motto should be followed: practise makes perfect! Additionally, through practising in this way you can learn to play the pieces from memory.

Rules of Notation

Up to the third line of the stave, note stems appear on the right of the note head, going up, and are approximately the length of three spaces (for example see bar 9). Notes above the middle line have stems on the left of the note head, going down (see bar 11).

Accompaniment: Take Five Fingers   With accompaniment, student plays one octave higher than written.

TAKE FIVE FINGERS

Track 10/11

Hans-Günter Heumann

Technique Tip:

Take care to continue playing legato when changing over from one hand to the other.

A **double bar line** divides a piece of music into sections.

Richard Wagner
(1813-1883)

Country: Germany
Period: Romantic
(1820-1900)
Works: 43

Wagner was the creator of the *Gesamtkunstwerk*, or total work of art – a type of music drama, combining poetry, music and theatre. He therefore wrote the texts and the stage directions of his 13 operas himself. He was the first composer to have had a festival opera house built for performances of his works, namely the *Ring Cycle* and *Parsifal*. Wagner was regarded as one of the most innovative European composers of the 19th century, particularly in terms of harmony and expression. Other famous operas by Wagner include: *The Flying Dutchman*, *Tannhauser*, *Lohengrin*, *The Mastersingers of Nuremberg* and *Tristan and Isolde*.

Theory Check 1   Name these notes.   See page 84 for answers

Accompaniment: Wedding March   With accompaniment, student plays one octave higher than written.

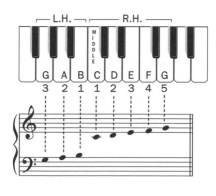

WEDDING MARCH

from the opera *Lohengrin*

Richard Wagner (1813-1883)
Arr.: Hans-Günter Heumann

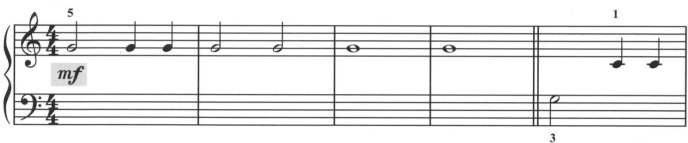

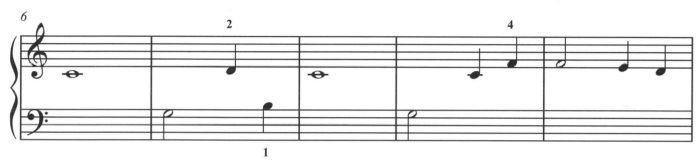

▪ Practice Tip:

Relaxed practice: Your posture and breathing are fundamental factors in achieving a relaxed approach to piano playing. You should sit so that the upper body is balanced and stable. Using the diaphragm to take consciously slow and regular breath is very important, breathing fresh air deeply into and out of the lungs. Certain muscle groups, such as those in the neck and shoulders, should consciously be relaxed.

mf **mezzoforte** = moderately loud

Wolfgang Amadeus Mozart (1756-1791)

Country: Austria
Period: Classical (1750-1820)
Works: over 600

Mozart was certainly one of the most versatile musical geniuses of all time. His concert tours through Europe, which began when he was very young, not only made him famous, but also exposed him to numerous styles of music. His father, Leopold, dedicated himself above all to the support and nurturing of his musical 'Wunderkinder', Wolfgang Amadeus and Maria Anna, known as *Nannerl*. Wolfgang Amadeus Mozart was one of the first self-employed musicians. His famous works include: *A Little Night Music* (*Eine kleine Nachtmusik*), *The Magic Flute*, *Piano Concerto No. 21*, *Clarinet Concerto*, *Prague Symphony*, *Jupiter Symphony*, *Turkish March* and his *Requiem*.

▪ Practice Tip:

Mental practice: From time to time, play (or think) through the piece in your head, and hear the music. In your mind's eye, imagine either the notation symbols or the fingers with which you play the notes.

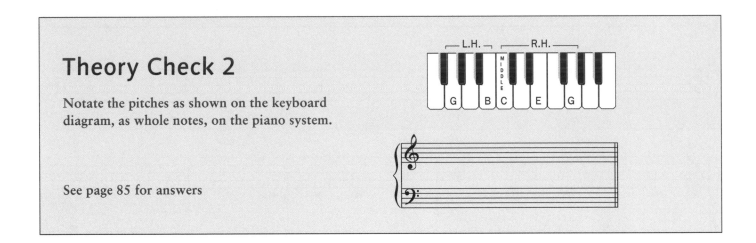

Theory Check 2

Notate the pitches as shown on the keyboard diagram, as whole notes, on the piano system.

See page 85 for answers

Accompaniment: A Little Night Music

With accompaniment, student plays one octave higher than written.

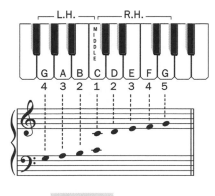

A Little Night Music

Theme from the 1st movement, K 525

Track 14/15

Wolfgang Amadeus Mozart (1756-1791)
Arr.: Hans-Günter Heumann

Allegro

The systematic index of Mozart's complete works is the so-called **Köchelverzeichnis** – named after Ludwig Ritter von Köchel – abbreviated with the letter **K**.

allegro = fast
An **Allegro** is a piece of music at a fast tempo.

RC/DC/FF More pieces in **Repertoire Collection, Duet Collection** and **Finger Fitness** see page 92

Lesson 6

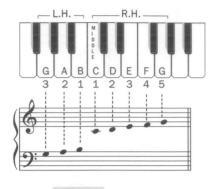

PASTORAL SONG

from Symphony No. 6, Op. 68

dolce = tenderly, sweetly

Ludwig van Beethoven (1770-1827)
Arr.: Hans-Günter Heumann

Dolce

Tie

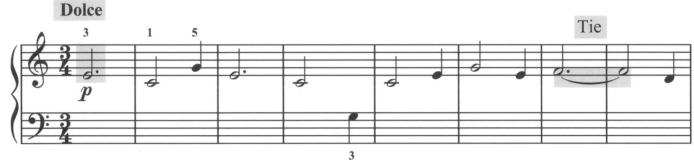

© 2012 Schott Music Limited, London

Accompaniment   With accompaniment, student plays one octave higher than written.

© 2012 Schott Music Limited, London

Dotted Half Note/Minim

clear note head →   ← stem
    ← dot after the note head

A **dotted half note** lasts for three beats. A dot after a note increases the note value by half as much again.

Tie

3/4

Count: 1 - 2 - 3   1 - 2 - 3
         clap hold hold   hold hold hold

A tie joins two notes of the same pitch. The tied note is not struck again, but held for the full combined duration.

Ludwig van Beethoven
(1770-1827)

Country: Germany
Period: Classical
(1750-1820)
Works: nearly 400

Beethoven is regarded as one of the most important composers of all time. Being one of the late Viennese Classical composers and paving the way for the Romantic period, the influence of his works is of the utmost significance. His virtuosic piano playing and his compositional talent attracted many patrons who supported him. In spite of his increasing deafness after 1802, he produced magnificent masterpieces. Some of his most famous works include: Symphony No. 3 – *Eroica*, Symphony No. 5 – *Fate Symphony*, Symphony No. 6 – *Pastoral*, Symphony No. 9 with the famous choral setting of Schiller's *Ode to Joy*, *Pathétique* and *Moonlight* piano sonatas, *Für Elise*, Piano Concerto No. 5, the Opera *Fidelio* and the *Kreutzer Sonata* for violin.

FINGER FITNESS 1

Hans-Günter Heumann

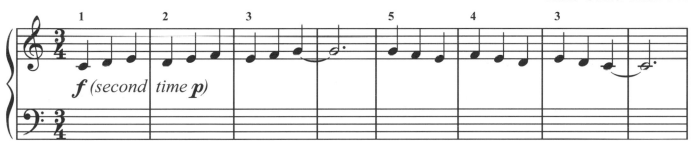

Accompaniment With accompaniment, student plays one octave higher than written.

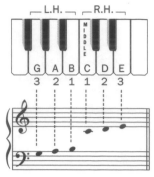

Twinkle, Twinkle, Little Star!

Track 20/21

This French song, dating from 1761, was used by Mozart in his 12 Variations *Ah, vous dirai-je, Maman* for piano.

French Melody
Arr.: Hans-Günter Heumann

A

f

Fine

B

mf

D.C. al Fine

D. C. al Fine = Da Capo al Fine   **Da Capo** (= from the beginning) means go back to the beginning and play until the word **Fine** (= end).

Accompaniment   With accompaniment, student plays one octave higher than written.

♩ = 100

f

Fine

mf

D.C. al Fine

2/4 Time

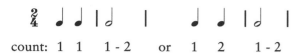

count: 1 1   1 - 2   or   1   2   1 - 2

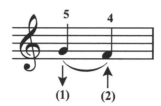

Technique Tip:

If two notes are joined with a slur, the first note (1) is played with a downwards movement of the arm and the second (2) with an upwards movement of the wrist.

Ternary Form: A–B–A

Ternary form is typical for many folk and children's songs, but is also found in classical music, e.g. in the symphony, sonata and in the so-called **Da capo Aria**. It has an A–B–A form, i.e. theme **A** is introduced, followed by a contrasting **B** theme, returning finally to the **A** theme.

Track 22/23

Hans-Günter Heumann

FINGER FITNESS 2

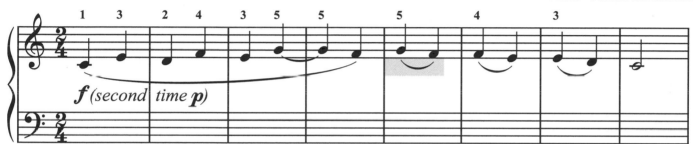

*f (second time **p**)*

© 2012 Schott Music Limited, London

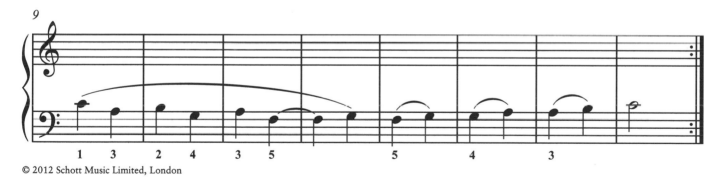

© 2012 Schott Music Limited, London

Accompaniment   With accompaniment, student plays one octave higher than written.

*f (second time **p**)*

© 2012 Schott Music Limited, London

RC/DC/FF   More pieces in **Repertoire Collection, Duet Collection** and **Finger Fitness** see page 92

Lesson 7

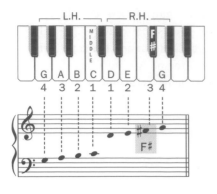

CANCAN

from the operetta *Orpheus in the Underworld*

Jacques Offenbach (1819 - 1880)
Arr.: Hans Günter Heumann

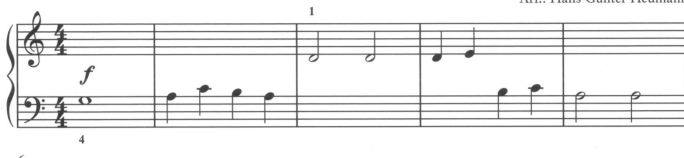

© 2012 Schott Music Limited, London

Accompaniment   With accompaniment, student plays one octave higher than written.

© 2012 Schott Music Limited, London

Jacques Offenbach
(1819-1880)

Country: France
Period: Romantic
(1820-1900)
Works: c. 100

Offenbach was born in Germany, but moved to Paris at the age of 14, where he remained for the rest of his life. He was the creator of the French Operetta. His works *La belle Hélène* and *Orpheus in the Underworld* (from which the famous *Cancan* comes), are amongst the most beautiful works of this genre. In the last year of his life, Offenbach wrote the opera *The Tales of Hoffmann*, though he did not live to see the premiere. Ernest Guiraud completed the score, following Offenbach's sketches. It includes a gondola scene during which the famous *Barcarolle* (see page 37) is performed.

Sharp Sign ♯

A **sharp sign** preceding a note raises it by a semitone. A **semitone/halftone** on the piano is the distance from one key to the next. You therefore play the next note to the right on the keyboard, whether it is a black or white key.

The sharp sign applies only during the bar in which it appears, i.e. from the note with the sharp sign to the next bar line.

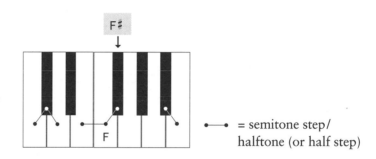

●—● = semitone step/ halftone (or half step)

Theory Check 3

Draw lines to connect the terms with their correct meanings.

allegro	quickly
D. C. al Fine	tenderly, sweetly
A-B-A	loud
forte	softly
dolce	ternary form
mezzoforte	indication to repeat from the beginning until the word *Fine*
piano	moderately loud

step

skip

repeated notes

See page 84 for answers

SURPRISE SYMPHONY

Theme from the 2nd movement of Symphony No. 94

Track 26/27

Joseph Haydn (1732-1809)
Arr.: Hans-Günter Heumann

Andante

Accompaniment

With accompaniment, student plays one octave higher than written.

Articulation is the joining and separating of notes. The two most important kinds of articulation are legato and staccato.

Staccato is a dot above or below the note. It means that the notes should be short and detached.

andante = at a walking pace
An **Andante** is also a piece of music with a moderately slow tempo.

pp pianissimo = very quiet

ff fortissimo = very loud

Symphony

In the middle of the 18th century, the symphony developed into an orchestral work with three or four movements in different tempos. The history of the symphony was greatly influenced by Joseph Haydn who wrote 104 of them.

Practice Tip: Structured practice: Study the piece, looking for repetitions and similarities.

Technique Tip: When playing staccato, the key is released quickly. The wrist makes a small, quick upwards movement. The finger then returns naturally to the key and rests there.

Joseph Haydn
(1732-1809)

Country: Austria
Period: Classical
(1750 -1820)
Works: around 1200

Alongside Mozart and Beethoven, Haydn was the oldest of the three Viennese classical composers. Haydn was a master of the forms of the symphony, string quartet and the oratorio, and he was a key figure in the development of the Classical style. At the age of 50, Europe lay at Haydn's feet. He was employed at the court of *Prince Esterházy* for nearly 30 years. Amongst his famous works are: *Surprise Symphony, Farewell Symphony, The Creation, The Seasons, Emperor Quartett.*

FINGER FITNESS 3

 Track 28/29

Hans-Günter Heumann

Accompaniment   With accompaniment, student plays one octave higher than written.

Lesson 8

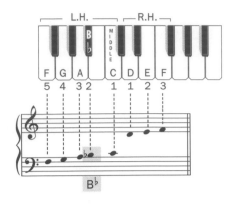

LONGING FOR SPRING

Track 30/31

Wolfgang Amadeus Mozart (1756-1791)
Arr.: Hans-Günter Heumann

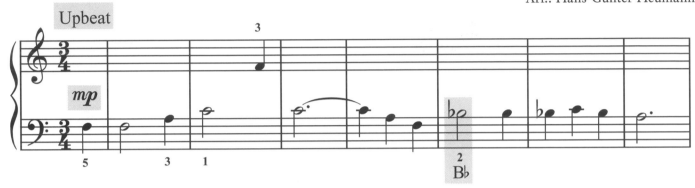

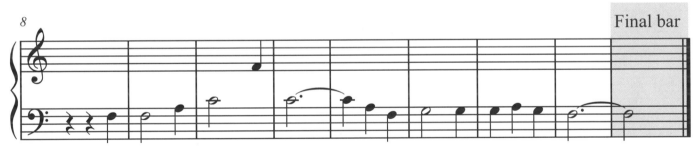

mp **mezzo piano** = moderately soft

Accompaniment With accompaniment, student plays one octave higher than written.

Flat Sign ♭

A **flat sign** before a note lowers it by a semitone / half-tone. Play the note immediately to the left on the keyboard – either black or white. It applies only during the bar in which it appears, that is from the note with the flat sign to the next bar-line.

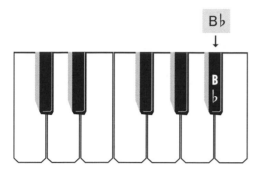

Upbeat

An **upbeat** or **anacrusis** is an incomplete bar at the beginning of a piece of music. Together with the final bar of the piece, it usually makes up a complete bar.

Example:

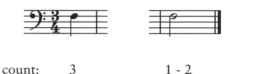

count: 3   1 - 2
        upbeat   +   final bar = complete bar

Theory Check 4

Fill in the answers to the questions below.

1. A sharp sign before a note _____ it by a semitone.

2. Explain the upper and lower figures of ¾ time:

   3 =
   4 =

3. A tie joins two notes of _____ pitch.

4. Is the tied note played again? _____

5. A flat sign before a note _____ it by a semitone / halftone.

6. Add the bar-lines to this melody:

7. What is an incomplete bar at the beginning of a piece of music called?

   _____

See page 84 for answers

Lesson 9

Playing with Hands together

▧ Practice and Technique Tips:

In the following piece, notes that appear directly above each other should be played at exactly the same time and released at the same time.

The hands move in opposite directions. One hand plays the notes rising in pitch (↗ upwards, or ascending – to the right of the keyboard), the other plays notes getting lower in pitch (↘ downwards or descending – to the left of the keyboard). This is called **contrary motion**.

Practice first with each hand separately, then with both hands together.

FINGER FITNESS 4

Hans-Günter Heumann

* See page 39 (Metronome)

© 2012 Schott Music Limited, London

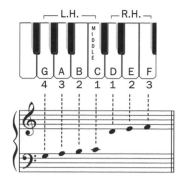

BARCAROLLE

from the opera *Tales of Hoffmann*

allegretto = moderately fast
An **Allegretto** is a musical piece at
a moderately fast tempo.

Jacques Offenbach (1819 - 1880)
Arr.: Hans Günter Heumann

Allegretto

4-bar introduction in the accompaniment

4-bar postlude in the accompaniment

Accompaniment With accompaniment, student plays one octave higher than written.

Sharps'n'Flats

♯ makes the notes higher

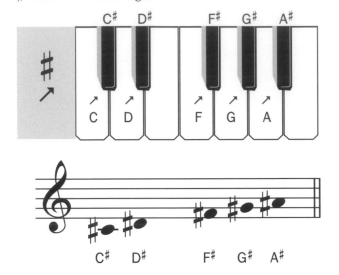

♭ makes the notes lower

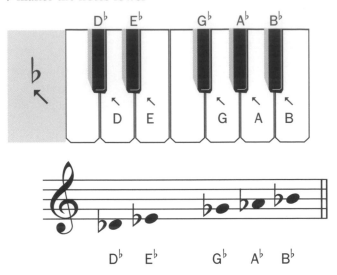

Theory Check 5

Before each note write a sharp or flat sign, depending on the direction of the arrow.

1.

2.

3.

4.

5.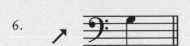

6.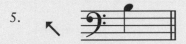

7.

8.

See page 85 for answers

DISCOVERY WALTZ

Track 35

Hans-Günter Heumann

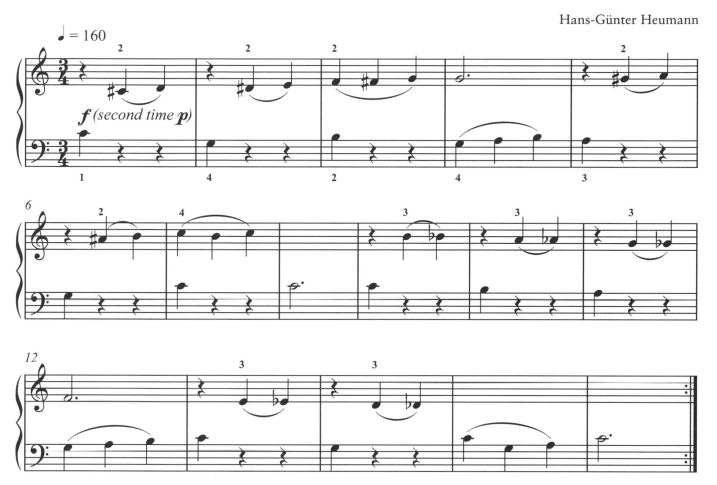

Metronome

The **metronome** is a mechanical or electronic device that indicates the beat, helping to control the tempo of a piece. Metronome markings are given at the beginning of a piece, for example ♩ = 100 quarter notes per minute. The device was invented in **1816** by **Johann Nepomuk Mälzel (1772-1838)**. Beethoven was the first to use the metronome in his music. He composed a canon for Mälzel, in which the clicking of the metronome was imitated. This melody also appears in the second movement of his eighth symphony.

RC/DC/FF More pieces in **Repertoire Collection, Duet Collection** and **Finger Fitness** see page 92

Lesson 10

Eighth note / Quaver

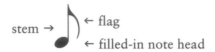

stem → ♪ ← flag
← filled-in note head

Two eighth notes / quavers equal the value of a quarter note.

♩ = 1 beat   ♪♪ = 1 beat

Several eighth notes / quavers are usually connected with a beam rather than each one having a flag. Eighth notes are played twice as fast as quarter notes. The second eighth note is counted with the syllable 'and'.

♪ ♪ = ♫ ← beam

count: 1   and   1 and

Rests

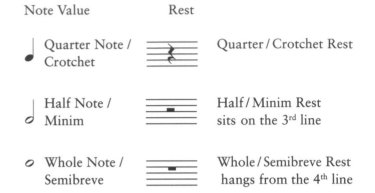

Rests are used in music to indicate moments of silence in the melody or accompaniment. The fingers are lifted from the keys. Each note has an equivalent rest.

Note Value		Rest
♩	Quarter Note / Crotchet	Quarter / Crotchet Rest
♩	Half Note / Minim	Half / Minim Rest sits on the 3rd line
o	Whole Note / Semibreve	Whole / Semibreve Rest hangs from the 4th line

Note: The whole rest corresponds with the duration of a complete bar whether in 2/4, 3/4 or 4/4-time.

---

crescendo, cresc. = gradually getting louder

♩ ♩ **Accent sign.** An **accent** above or below a note means that you should play the note with emphasis.

▪ Technique Tip: When producing a crescendo, depress the keys fully with increasing arm weight.

Accompaniment: Turkish March With accompaniment, student plays one octave higher than written.

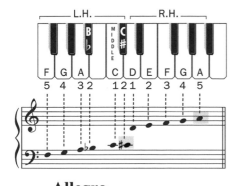

TURKISH MARCH

from *Ruins of Athens,* Op. 113

 Track 36/37

Ludwig van Beethoven (1770 - 1827)
Arr.: Hans Günter Heumann

Allegro

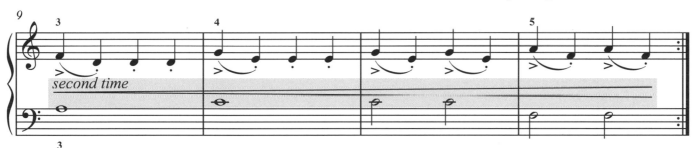

Theory Check 6

Mark with a cross where applicable.

See page 85 for answers

1. What does staccato mean?

☐ play smoothly

☐ play moderately quickly

☐ play short and detatched

2. Which dynamic marking is the quietest?

☐ *p*

☐ *mp*

☐ *pp*

3. How many beats does the dotted half note last for? 𝅗𝅥.

☐ 1

☐ 2

☐ 3

Minuet

Track 38

Jean-Philippe Rameau (1683 - 1764)
Arr.: Hans Günter Heumann

Moderato ♩ = 108

The **minuet** was the most popular courtly dance in the 17th and 18th centuries. At the French court of Louis XIV, 'Sun King' it became one of the most distinguished dance forms. The minuet is a partner dance in a moderately fast ¾-time. It is characterised by small steps, intricate patterns and bows.

moderato = moderately fast, but slightly slower than allegretto

Moderato can also be used as the title of a piece to be played at a moderately fast tempo.

Jean-Philippe Rameau (1683-1764)

Country: France
Period: Baroque (1600-1750)
Works: around 100

Rameau – a contemporary of Bach, Handel and Telemann – was one of the most important and versatile musicians of the first half of the 18th century and also one of the most important music theoreticians of his time. In 1722 he wrote his famous *Traité de l'harmonie* and with this established the theoretical basis of modern harmony. He was also a master of harpsichord music and composed four volumes of *Pièces de clavecin*. Central to Rameau's work was opera, a form to which he turned only at the age of 50. From then up until his death, he created over 20 stage works, reinvigorating French opera and in so doing followed on from his predecessor Jean-Baptiste Lully.

PRESTO

Track 39

Daniel Gottlob Türk (1750-1813)

Octave Transposition Sign

8 - - - - - ⌐   or   *8va* - - - - - ⌐

Play the note or notes below which this sign appears, an **octave** (= 8 notes) higher than written. This applies until the end of the broken line.

presto = very fast
A **Presto** is also a piece with a very fast tempo.

■ Technique Tip:

The octave transposition indication in the R. H. corresponds with a natural extension of the forearm.

Daniel Gottlob Türk (1750-1813)

Country: Germany
Period: Classical (1750-1820)
Works: over 100

Türk, a contemporary of Mozart and Haydn, was a highly regarded pedagogue, music director, and writer of theoretical and didactic musical works. Amongst his most well known works are the piano method of 1789 and a large collection of piano compositions of what were called 'Handstücke' (pieces for the hand). These were short, individual pieces, for educational purposes, to supplement finger exercises. Türk founded the *Collegium musicum* and, through regular concerts he supported the work of contemporary musicians such as Mozart and Haydn, but above all, he was responsible for generating a renewed interest in the music of Bach and Handel.

PRELUDE from *Te Deum*

Marc-Antoine Charpentier (c. 1643-1704)
Arr.: Hans-Günter Heumann

Marc-Antoine Charpentier (c. 1643-1704)

Country: France
Period: Baroque (1600-1750)
Works: over 500

Charpentier went to Rome in 1662, to study with Giacomo Carissimi – one of the most famous Italian composers of that time. His distinctive style therefore combined French and Italian traditions. He was supported by Mademoiselle de Guise, who employed many musicians in her court. Despite many attempts, he was never offered employment at the court of Louis XIV; he finally became Director of Music at the Sainte-Chapelle in Paris. Charpentier composed primarily for the church, and the theatre where he worked with Molière. His most famous work is the *Prelude* from the *Te Deum* in D major, which, since 1954, has been used as the Eurovision signature-tune.

ritardando, **rit.** or **ritard.** = gradually getting slower

Dotted Quarter Note/Crotchet

filled-in note head→ ●• ←stem
↖dot after the note head

A dotted quarter note/crotchet lasts for 1½ beats,
as the dot after a note lengths it by half its value.

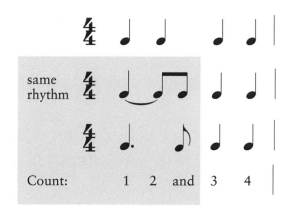

Theory Check 7

Mark with a cross or fill in the answers to the questions below.

1. If a piece should be played
very quickly, which tempo
marking would be used?

☐ allegretto

☐ allegro

☐ presto

Fill in the correct answers.

2. A dot after a note lengthens
it by _____ its value.

3. Which note value is equal
to the dot after a quarter note?

_____

4. Draw lines to indicate the correct answers:

pp   play an octave higher than
                            written.

rit.   very softly

8̶ ̶ ̶ ̶ ̶ ┐   gradually getting louder

cresc.   gradually getting slower

▬▬▬   half rest

▬▬▬   whole rest

See page 85 for answers

RC/DC/FF ▶ More pieces in **Repertoire Collection, Duet Collection** and **Finger Fitness** see page 92

Lesson 11

C Major 5-Note Pattern

● **Major** indicates a particular musical tonality.

● The construction of the major pattern is as follows:

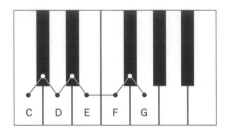

● — ● = half step

> ### The Construction of the Major 5-Note Pattern:
>
> Whole Step Whole Step Half Step Whole Step
>   W   W   H   W

From the note C to D = 2 halftone steps = 1 whole step
From the note D to E = 2 halftone steps = 1 whole step
From the note E to F = 1 halftone step = 1 half step
From the note F to G = 2 halftone steps = 1 whole step

● A distinguishing feature of the major tonality is the distance (= **interval**) of 4 semitone / half steps from the key note.

● The aural impression of the major tonality is bright, clear and happy.

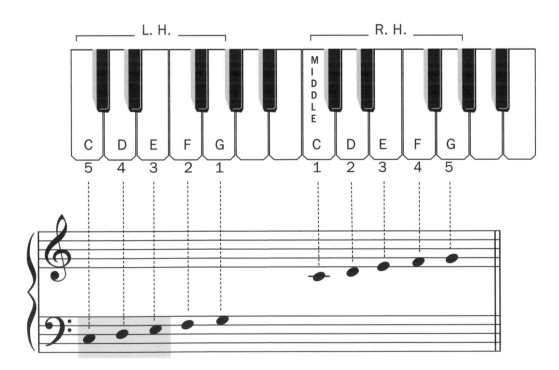

Playing Tips:

In the first 8 bars of this exercise the melody moves in the same direction – upwards and downwards – in both hands. This is known as **parallel motion**.

In bars 9-16 one part in either hand is held, while the other part moves upwards or downwards. This is known as **lateral motion**.

FINGER FITNESS 5

Play hands separately, first.

Hans-Günter Heumann

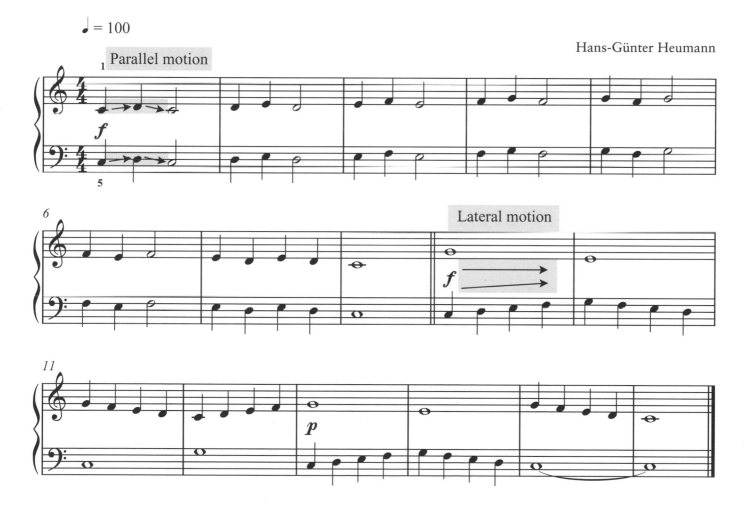

MUSETTE

 Track 42

from *Notebook for
Anna Magdalena Bach*

Musette is the term for the French bagpipes of the 17th and 18th centuries, or a dance performed to the accompaniment of this instrument.

Johann Sebastian Bach (1685-1750)
Arr.: Hans-Günter Heumann

♩ = 144

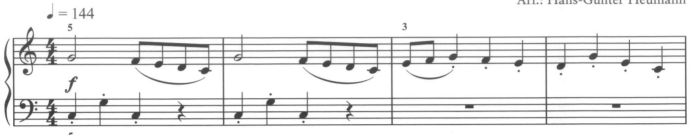

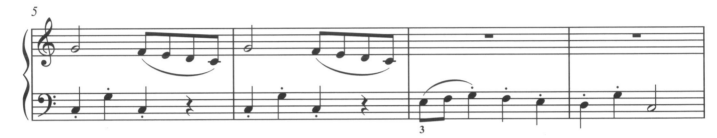

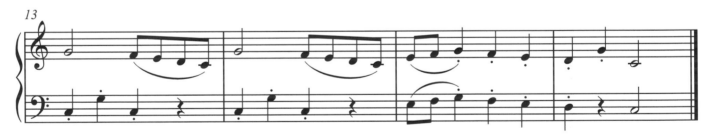

Johann Sebastian Bach
(1685-1750)

Country: Germany
Period: Baroque
(1600-1750)
Works: over 1000

Bach is regarded as one of the greatest composers in musical history. In his time he was known above all as a choirmaster and organist, becoming gradually better known as a composer. It was not until the 19th century that his true worth was recognized. Bach, who had a very busy working life, was appropriately referred to in an obituary by Georg Philipp Telemann as 'the great master of counterpoint and the art of the organ, the inventive improviser and educator of distinguished sons and students'. Some of his most famous works are: The *Well-Tempered Clavier*, *Goldberg Variations*, *St Matthew* and *St John Passions*, Mass in B Minor, Toccata and Fugue in D Minor and the *Brandenburg Concertos*.

SPRING

from *The Four Seasons*

Track 43

Antonio Vivaldi (1678-1741)
Arr.: Hans-Günter Heumann

Allegro ♩ = 160

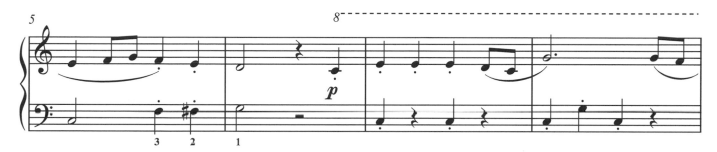

Antonio Vivaldi
(1678-1741)

Country: Italy
Period: Baroque
(1600-1750)
Works: over 800

Vivaldi, who was taught music by his father, a violinist at St Mark's Basilica in Venice, in 1703 was ordained to the priesthood. He was nicknamed the *Red Priest* because of the colour of his hair. From 1714-1740 he was the composer-in-residence of the *Ospedale della Pietà*, a conservatoire for orphans in Venice. His concerts with the highly regarded conservatoire orchestra quickly became famous. As well as being one of the most important Italian baroque composers, Vivaldi was also highly prolific, writing over 800 concertos, operas, sacred vocal works as well as other instrumental works. In addition, he was one of the greatest violin virtuosos of his time. His most famous works include: *The Four Seasons* and *Gloria*.

RC/DC/FF More pieces in **Repertoire Collection**, **Duet Collection** and **Finger Fitness** see page 93

Lesson 12

Intervals

An **interval** is the distance between two notes.

 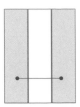 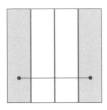 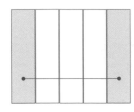

Second
distance of 2 notes

Third
distance of 3 notes

Fourth
distance of 4 notes

Fifth
distance of 5 notes

Intervals are heard
1. In succession – melodic interval Two notes sound one after another as a melody, either upwards or downwards.

L = Line S = Space

2. Together – harmonic interval Two notes sound together, producing harmony.

FINGER FITNESS 6

 Track 44

Hans-Günter Heumann

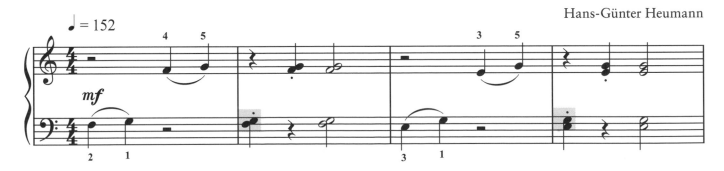

© 2012 Schott Music Limited, London

Scherzo

Track 45

from *Melodious Exercises* Op. 149, No. 6

Anton Diabelli (1781-1858)
Arr.: Hans-Günter Heumann

decrescendo, decresc. = gradually getting softer

Anton Diabelli
(1781-1858)

Country: Austria
Period: Classical
(1750-1820)
Works: over 200

Diabelli was a music publisher, music teacher and composer in Vienna and studied with Michael Haydn, then later with his brother Joseph Haydn. He wrote operas, sacred and secular music, as well as songs and piano works. Only the piano pieces – solos, but particularly the duets – have established themselves in the repertoire, such as the *Melodious Exercises*, Op. 149. He became more famous, however, through the work of another composer, than through his own, providing the central theme for Beethoven's *33 Variations on a Waltz by Diabelli* (also known as the *Diabelli Variations*), Op. 120.

G Major 5-Note Pattern

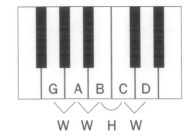

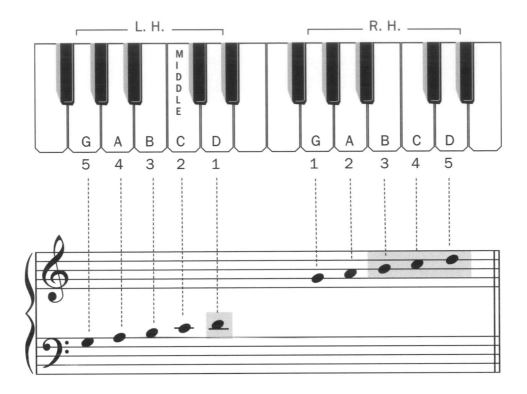

FINGER FITNESS 7

Play hands separately, first.

♩ = 160

Hans-Günter Heumann

Ode to Joy

from Symphony No. 9

Ludwig van Beethoven (1770-1827)
Arr.: Hans-Günter Heumann

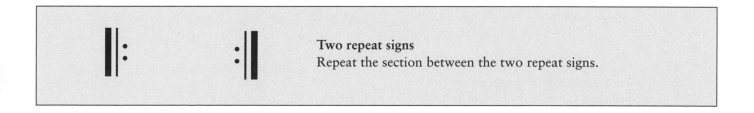

Two repeat signs
Repeat the section between the two repeat signs.

RC/DC/FF   More pieces in **Repertoire Collection**, **Duet Collection** and **Finger Fitness** see page 93

Lesson 13

Triads

- A **triad** consists of three notes: the **key note** (or **tonic**), **third** and **fifth**.

- The notes of a triad are notated either on three lines, or in three spaces.

- The lowest note, the **key note**, is also the name of the triad or chord.

- A **chord** is produced when three or more notes of different pitch sound together.

C major Triad / Chord

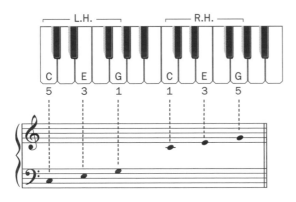

G major Triad / Chord

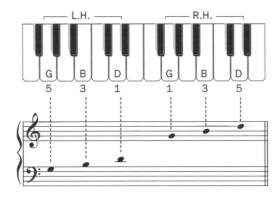

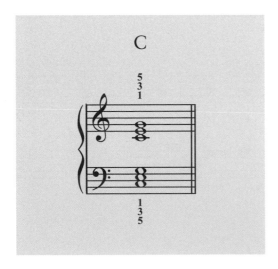

- The **chord symbol** is derived from the key note. The chord symbol C means a C major triad and the chord symbol G means a G major triad.

FINGER FITNESS 8

Hans-Günter Heumann

Transposing

Transposing means moving a piece of music from one key into another, retaining the intervals and other distinguishing features of the original.

Transpose the exercise also into the G pattern.

simile, sim. = similarly – continue in the same way

AIR from *Water Music*

Track 49

George Frideric Handel (1685-1759)
Arr.: Hans Günter Heumann

The term **Air** (Fr. = melody) was used in the 16th and 17th centuries to refer to a solo song with lute accompaniment. Later on the name was also used for instrumental pieces with tuneful melodies, which might be included in a suite. A suite is a composition consisting of a sequence of several dance movements.

George Frideric Handel
(1685-1759)

Country: Germany
Period: Baroque
(1600-1750)
Works: around 500

Handel was one of the main representatives of the Baroque period. In contrast to Bach, who came from the same region, and who was born at the same time, Handel was drawn to the wider world. In Italy he was greatly inspired by his musical experiences and he himself had a great influence over English musical life for almost 50 years. He successfully promoted his operas through his own opera company. When interest in serious Italian opera – so-called *opera seria* – diminished, he turned to the form of the *oratorio*. Handel was without doubt one of the most important opera and oratorio composers of his time. However, there are also great masterpieces amongst his instrumental compositions. Some of his most famous works are: *Water Music, Music for the Royal Fireworks*, the opera *Xerxes* and the oratorio *Messiah*.

Theory Check 8

Fill in the answers to the questions below.

1. Write down an alternative way of notating the following rhythm:

_____

2. What is the abbreviation for gradually getting slower?

_____

3. How is the major 5-note pattern constructed?

_____ _____ _____ _____

4. Fill in the half step (H) and the whole steps (W):

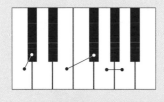

___ ___ ___

5. What is the term for the movement of the parts in this example?

_____

6. Name the intervals below:

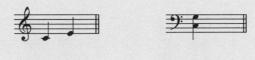

_____ _____

_____ _____

7. Connect the terms with their meanings.

simile   means moving a piece
                           of music from one key
                           into another

decresc.   gradually getting louder

cresc.   moderately fast

moderato   gradually getting softer

transposing   similar – continue in
                           the same way

8. Add the stems:

See page 86 for answers

D Major 5-Note Pattern

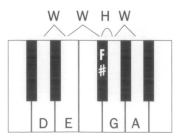

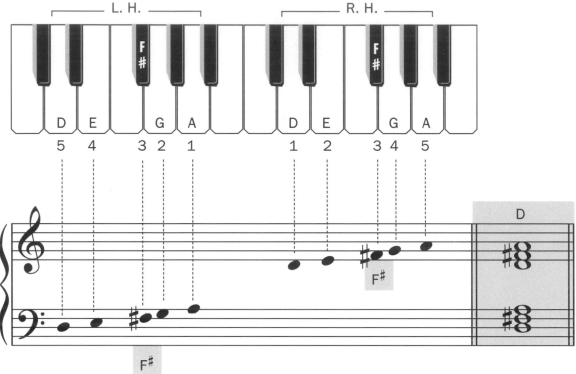

FINGER FITNESS 9

Track 50

Play hands separately, first.

Hans-Günter Heumann

TRUMPET TUNE *from The Indian Queen*

 Track 51

Henry Purcell (1659-1695)
Arr.: Hans-Günter Heumann

© 2012 Schott Music Limited, London

Henry Purcell
(1659-1695)

Country: England
Period: Baroque
(1600-1750)
Works: over 500

Purcell is one of the most important English composers. From an early age he held highly regarded positions both at the English court and the church. At the age of 18 he was a court composer, two years later he was appointed organist at Westminster Abbey, and shortly after that he was appointed to the chapel Royal. As court composer, it was Purcell's duty to write pieces for royal festivities. In spite of his short life, he created a great many works in a variety of different genres: an opera, *Dido and Aeneas*, other semi-operas, incidental theatre music, anthems, court odes, secular songs, choral works, chamber music and pieces for organ.

F Major 5-Note Pattern

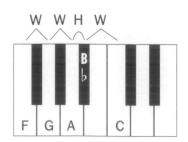

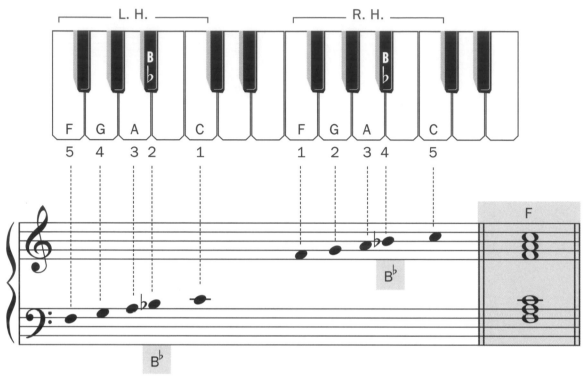

FINGER FITNESS 10

Play hands separately, first.

Hans-Günter Heumann

FOR NANNERL

Freely adapted from the original version from the
Notebook for Nannerl by Leopold Mozart.

Track 53

Leopold Mozart
(1719-1787)
Arr.: Hans-Günter Heumann

Transpose the piece into other 5-note patterns:

C Major 5-Note Pattern

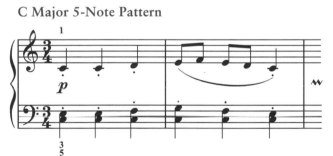

G Major 5-Note Pattern

Leopold Mozart
(1719-1787)

Country: Austria
Period: Classical
(1750-1820)
Works: over 500

Leopold Mozart was Deputy Kapellmeister for the court in Salzburg, a violinist, teacher and author of an important treatise on violin playing, and a composer, as well as being the father of the famous Wolfgang Amadeus Mozart. Some of his works are still performed today, including: *Musical Sleigh Ride*, *Toy Symphony*, *The Peasant Wedding*, *Hunting Symphony*, Flute Concerto in G Major and the Trumpet Concerto in D Major. Historically he is remembered primarily as the tireless supporter, educator, teacher and travel companion of his musical 'Wunderkinder'. In 1759 he created a 'Notebook' (familiarly *Notenbuch*) for his daughter Maria Anna, known as *Nannerl*. The piano pieces in this collection also provided her younger brother with practice material.

Largo

Theme from *The New World Symphony*

Track 54

Antonín Dvořák (1841-1904)
Arr.: Hans-Günter Heumann

largo = very slow, steady, stately   A **Largo** is a piece of music with a slow, steady tempo.

Antonín Dvořák
(1841-1904)

Country:
Czech Republic
Period: Romantic
(1820-1900)
Works:
around 200

Dvořák was perhaps the most successful of the Nationalist composers of the 19th century in integrating elements of folk music into classical forms. He was celebrated as a hero of Slavonic music, and Brahms, in particular, gave him such support that interest for his music spread quickly, first in Europe, then also in the USA. Subsequently, Dvořák went to New York, as Director of the National Conservatory of Music, where he composed his famous last symphony, *From the New World*. Other famous works from his repertoire are: *Slavonic Dances*, *Stabat mater*, the opera *Rusalka* and the Cello Concerto.

Theory Check 9   Fill in the answers to the questions below.

1. Which three notes create a triad?   _____   _____   _____

2. A chord is a combination of at least _____ or _____ notes of different pitches.

3. The chord symbol is named after the _____ .

4. Name the following triads: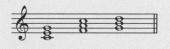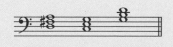

   ___ ___ ___   ___ ___ ___

See page 86 for answers

RC/DC/FF   More pieces in **Repertoire Collection**, **Duet Collection** and **Finger Fitness** see page 94

Composer Check   Mark with a cross where applicable.

1. Which composers lived in the Classical period?

☐ a) Schubert, Schumann, Chopin

☐ b) Haydn, Mozart, Beethoven

☐ c) Bach, Handel, Telemann

2. Who composed the famous serenade *Eine kleine Nachtmusik*?

☐ a) Ludwig van Beethoven

☐ b) Joseph Haydn

☐ c) Wolfgang Amadeus Mozart

3. Which composer began composing operas seriously only from the age of 50?

☐ a) Giuseppe Verdi

☐ b) Giacomo Puccini

☐ c) Jean-Philippe Rameau

4. Put the following periods of musical history in the correct chronological order:

☐ a) Romantic

☐ b) Baroque

☐ c) Classical

5. Which composer had a Festival Hall built for his own works in Bayreuth?

☐ a) Richard Wagner

☐ b) Ludwig van Beethoven

☐ c) Jacques Offenbach

6. Who composed the famous piano piece *Für Elise*?

☐ a) Joseph Haydn

☐ b) Ludwig van Beethoven

☐ c) Wolfgang Amadeus Mozart

7. Which composer was given the nickname the *Red Priest*?

☐ a) Johann Sebastian Bach

☐ b) Antonio Vivaldi

☐ c) George Frideric Handel

8. Which opera did Wolfgang Amadeus Mozart compose?

☐ a) The Magic Flute

☐ b) Fidelio

☐ c) The Flying Dutchman

9. What is the name of the composer whose famous last symphony *From the New World* was composed in the USA?

☐ a) Henry Purcell

☐ b) Edvard Grieg

☐ c) Antonín Dvořák

10. Which composer became more famous through the work of another composer than through his own works?

☐ a) Marc-Antoine Charpentier

☐ b) Daniel Gottlob Türk

☐ c) Anton Diabelli

Answers: 1b, 2c, 3c, 4bca, 5a, 6b, 7b, 8a, 9c, 10c

Lesson 14

A Minor 5-Note Pattern

- **Minor** describes a musical mode.

- Minor and major are both modes, which became prevalent in the 17th century as opposed to the various church modes that were previously favoured. This is known as the **major-minor system**.

- The construction of the minor mode pattern is as follows:

> **The Construction of the Minor 5-Note Pattern:**
>
> | Whole Step | Half Step | Whole Step | Whole Step |
> |:---:|:---:|:---:|:---:|
> | W | H | W | W |

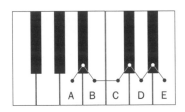

⟶ = half step/
semitone step

From the note A to B = 2 half steps = 1 whole step
From the note B to C = 1 half step = 1 half step
From the note C to D = 2 half steps = 1 whole step
From the note D to E = 2 half steps = 1 whole step

The interval that characterizes the minor mode is that of three semitones / half steps from the key note (or tonic), known as the minor third, as opposed to the major third.

The aural impression of the minor tonality is dark, gloomy and sad.

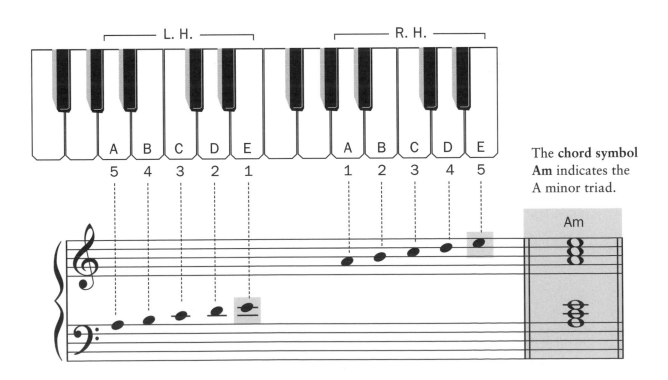

The **chord symbol Am** indicates the A minor triad.

La Marmotte

from Op. 52

Track 55

Ludwig van Beethoven (1770-1827)
Arr.: Hans-Günter Heumann

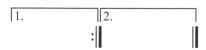

If the end of a repeated section is different to the first time, numbered brackets can be added. The first time you play the part beneath bracket 1, the next time you miss out bracket 1 and immediately go on to bracket 2.

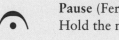 **Pause** (Fermata)
Hold the note on a little longer.

Sentimental Dialogue

Hans-Günter Heumann

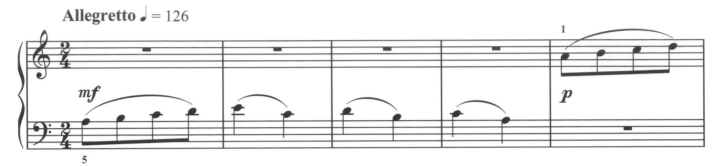

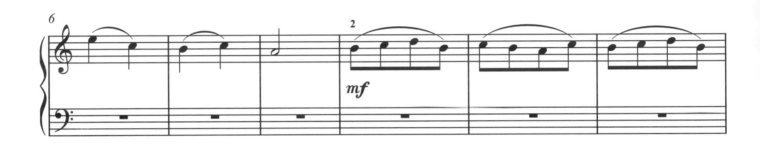

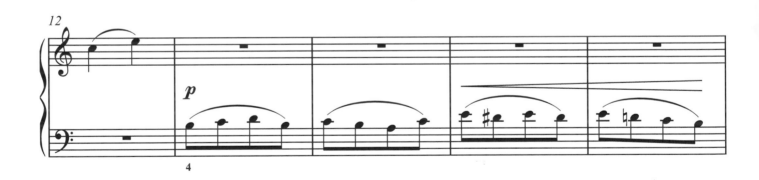

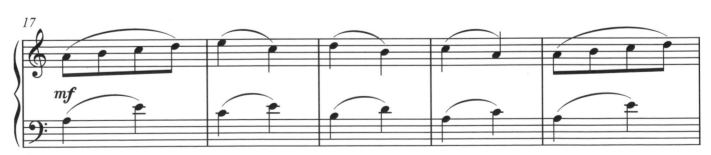

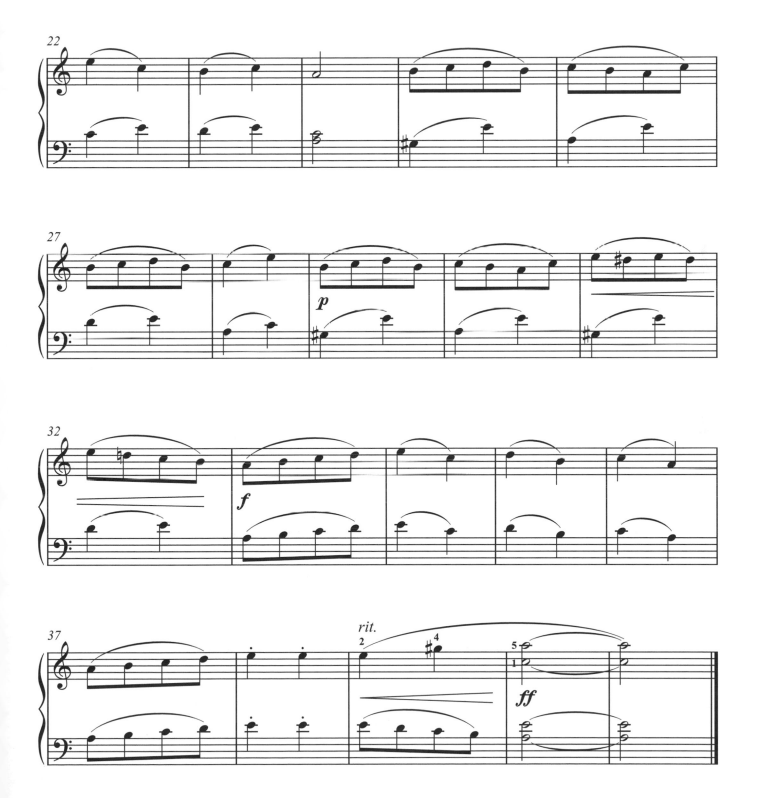

E Minor 5-Note Pattern

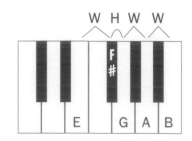

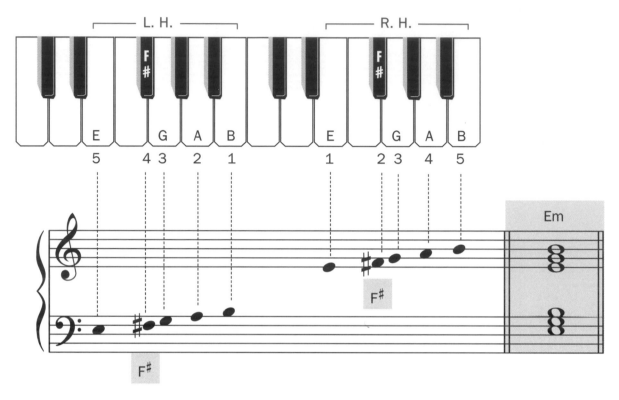

FINGER FITNESS 11

Play hands separately, first.

Hans-Günter Heumann

BOURRÉE

from Suite No. 1 for Lute

Johann Sebastian Bach (1685-1750)
Arr.: Hans-Günter Heumann

The **Bourrée** was originally a French folk dance, which became a courtly dance around 1560 and was popular until well into the 18th century.

Natural sign ♮

A **natural sign** cancels both flat and sharp signs, meaning that you return to playing the original white key.

SYMPHONY NO.1

Theme from the 3rd movement

Gustav Mahler (1860-1911)
Arr.: Hans-Günter Heumann

*) 2nd finger crosses over the thumb.

This symphony by Mahler begins with a quotation of the famous French children's song *Frère Jacques*. However, Mahler's version appears in the minor rather than major and therefore sounds rather like a funeral march.

Gustav Mahler
(1860-1911)

Country: Austria
Period:
Late Romantic
Works: 18

Mahler was one of the most important composers of the late Romantic period, and also one of the most famous conductors of his time. As an opera director – especially at the Vienna Court Opera – he reformed and revolutionized music theatre. After holding many important positions as a director of music throughout Europe, in 1907 he was appointed musical director at the Metropolitan Opera House in New York. In 1911 he returned to Vienna, suffering from heart disease, and died later that year. Amongst his most famous works are the nine symphonies as well as the orchestral song cycle 'Das Lied von der Erde' and songs such as 'Lieder eines fahrenden Gesellen', songs from 'Des Knaben Wunderhorn' and the 'Kindertotenlieder'. He extended the orchestra in terms of tone colour as well as in size, his eighth symphony therefore being called the 'Symphony of a Thousand'.

DANCE OF THE LITTLE SWANS

From the ballet *Swan Lake*

Track 60

Pyotr Ilyich Tchaikovsky
(1840-1893)
Arr.: Hans-Günter Heumann

*) 3rd finger crosses over the thumb.

Pyotr Ilyich Tchaikovsky (1840-1893)

Country: Russia
Period: Romantic (1820-1900)
Works: Over 150

Tchaikovsky first attended law school in St Petersburg and became a civil servant. At the same time he studied music privately. Soon he dedicated himself exclusively to music, studying with Anton Rubinstein at the St Petersburg Conservatoire, where he also later taught. He composed and conducted his own works and eventually became one of the leading Russian composers of the 19th century. Amongst his most famous works are the Piano Concerto No. 1, Violin Concerto, Symphony No. 6 – *Pathétique*, *Serenade for strings*, *Capriccio Italien*, the ballets *Swan Lake*, *Sleeping Beauty* and *The Nutcracker*; the operas *Eugen Onegin* and *Pique Dame* and piano works such as *The Seasons* and *Album for the Young*.

D Minor 5-Note Pattern

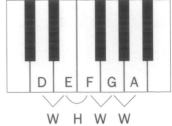

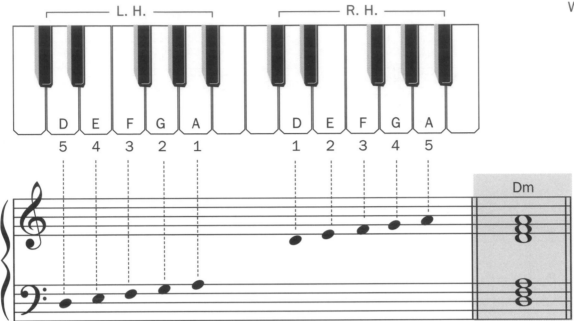

FINGER FITNESS 12

Track 61

Play hands separately, first.

Hans-Günter Heumann

Theory Check 10

Fill in the answers to the questions below.

1. What are the two most common modes used in music? _____ _____

2. What is the construction of the minor 5-note pattern? _____ _____ _____ _____

3. What are the names of these notes?

— — — — — — — — —

4. Draw lines to connect the symbols with their meanings:

⌢   work, composition

♮   natural sign

♯   cresc.

♭   decresc.

Op.   pause

_____   flat sign

_____   sharp sign

5. Add the names of the major or minor patterns shown:

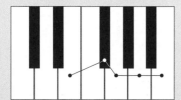   

_____   _____

See page 86 for answers

Symphony No. 7

Theme from the 2nd movement, Op. 92

Ludwig van Beethoven (1770-1827)
Arr.: Hans-Günter Heumann

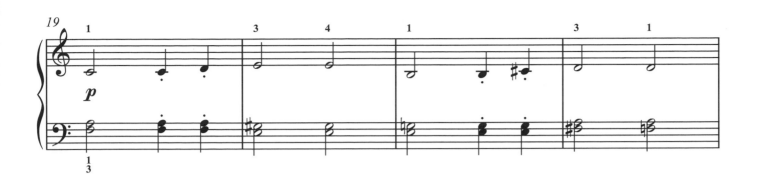

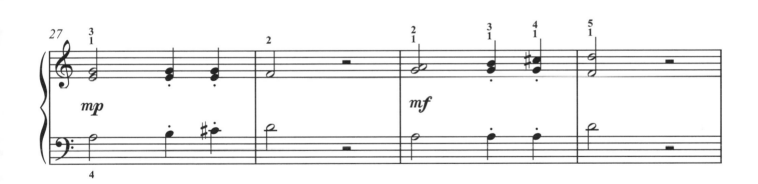

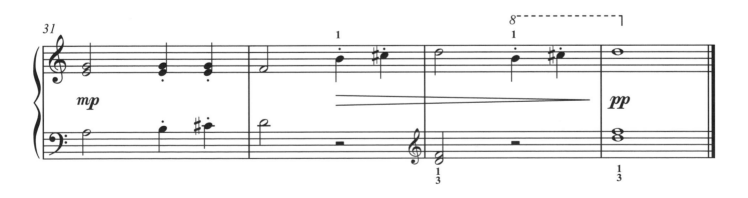

RC/DC/FF More pieces in **Repertoire Collection**, **Duet Collection** and **Finger Fitness** see page 94

Lesson 15

The Right Pedal (Sustaining Pedal)

- The right pedal, also known as the sustaining pedal, is used to sustain and connect notes. When you depress the pedal, the felt dampers are raised from the strings, so that all the strings can vibrate freely, and the notes sound for longer.

- The sustaining pedal is used with the right foot. The heel remains firmly on the ground and the ball of the foot remains in contact with the pedal.

- The pedalling symbol is a bracket, which shows you exactly how and when to use the pedal.

- The pedal is usually used after the keys are depressed.

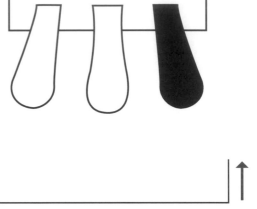

depress
the pedal

hold the pedal
down

release the
pedal

Pedal Exercise 1

Process:
- Play the note C
- After playing the note – on beat 2 – depress the pedal
- Hold the pedal down
- As you play the next note, raise the pedal
- Then immediately press the pedal down again
- etc. (simile)

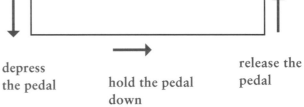

Pedalling as follows: ⌐_____⌐_____⌐ *simile*
Actual pedalling
as indicated: ⌐_____⌐_____⌐ *simile*
Count: 1   2   3   change pedal

Pedal Exercise 2

- Repeat the exercise above playing chords with the R. H.

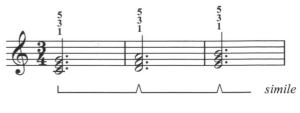

change pedal   change pedal

SOUND PAINTING

Hans-Günter Heumann

Longing For You

Hans-Günter Heumann

poco moto = with a little movement   ɤ = Eighth rest/Quaver rest

DREAM OF LOVE

No. 3, Theme

Track 65

Franz Liszt (1811-1886)
Arr.: Hans-Günter Heumann

Poco allegro con affetto ♩ = 120

Franz Liszt
(1811-1886)

Country: Hungary
Period: Romantic
(1820-1900)
Works: Over 700

Liszt was a pupil of the famous piano pedagogue Carl Czerny (who himself was a pupil of Beethoven) and performed concerts from an early age throughout Europe. He was without doubt one of the greatest piano virtuosos of all time and paved the way for the modern concert pianist. He created orchestral sounds with the piano. He undertook extensive concert tours before his appointment as Hofkapellmeister in Weimar in 1847, where he also composed his most significant works.

He supported musicians and taught many well-known pianists and renowned piano pedagogues. In later years he took on the modest post of Abbé, whilst continuing to compose, teach and perform until his death.

Amongst his most famous works are the Sonata for Piano in B minor, Transcendental Studies (dedicated, with gratitude, to his teacher Czerny), the *Mephisto Waltz* No. 1, *Liebestraum (Dream of Love)* No. 3, *Années de Pèlerinage*, Hungarian Rhapsody No. 2, study *La Campanella*, Consolation No. 3, Piano Concerto No. 1 and the symphonic poem *Les Préludes*.

RC/DC/FF More pieces in **Repertoire Collection**, **Duet Collection** and **Finger Fitness** see page 94

Theory Check Solutions

Theory Check 1

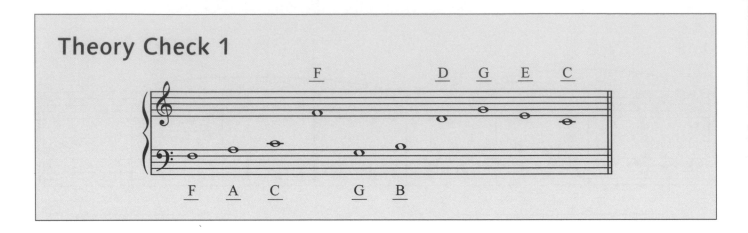

Theory Check 3

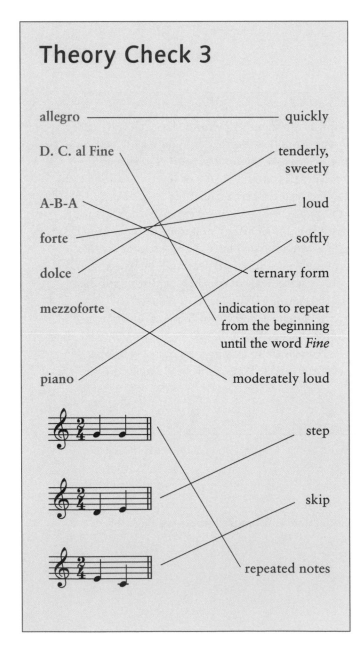

Theory Check 4

1. A sharp sign before a note raises it by a semitone/halftone.

2. Explain the upper and lower figures of 𝟑⁄𝟒 time:

   3 = 3 beats per bar
   4 = A quarter note forms the beat.

3. A tie joins two notes of the same pitch.

4. Is the tied note played again? No.

5. A flat sign before a note lowers it by a semitone/halftone.

6. Add the bar-lines to this melody:

7. What is an incomplete bar at the beginning of a piece of music called?
   Upbeat or anacrusis

Theory Check 2

Theory Check 5

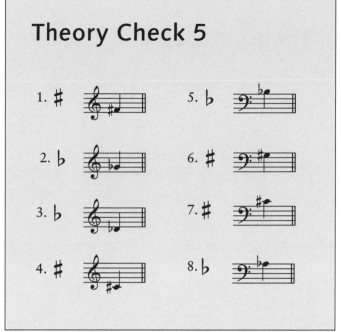

Theory Check 6

1. What does staccato mean?
   Play short and detatched

2. Which dynamic marking is the quietest? *pp*

3. How many beats does this note
   (dotted half note/minim) last for? 3

Theory Check 7

1. If a piece should be played very quickly,
   which tempo marking would be used?
   presto

2. A dot after a note lengthens
   it by half its value.

3. Which note value is equal to the dot
   after a quarter note?
   eighth note

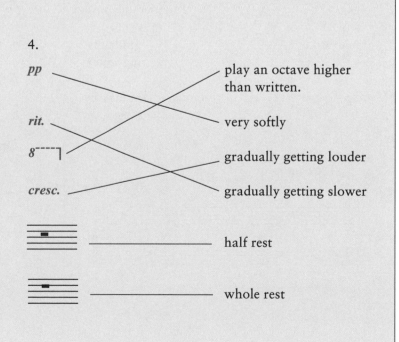

Theory Check 8

1.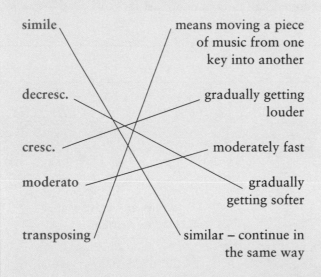

2. rit. or ritard.

3. W   W   H   W

4. H   W   W

5. Parallel motion

6. third
   fifth
   second
   fourth

7. Connect the terms with their meanings:

simile — similar – continue in the same way

decresc. — gradually getting louder

cresc. — moderately fast

moderato — means moving a piece of music from one key into another

transposing — gradually getting softer

(the term "means moving a piece of music from one key into another" connects to transposing; "gradually getting louder" connects to cresc.; "moderately fast" connects to moderato; "gradually getting softer" connects to decresc.; "similar – continue in the same way" connects to simile)

8. Add the stems:

Theory Check 9

1. Key note (tonic), third, fifth

2. three, more

3. key note

4. Treble clef: C major, F major, G major
   Bass clef: D major, C major, G major

Theory Check 10

1. What are the two most common modes used in music? Major, minor

2. What is the construction of the minor 5-note pattern? W H W W

3. What are the names of these notes?
   G#, F, C D#, E, Ab, Gb, D, E, C#

4. Draw lines to connect the symbols with their meanings:

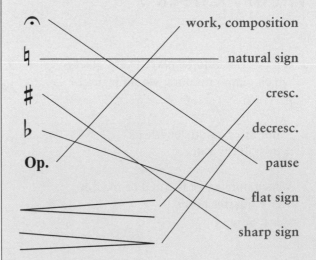

5. E minor pattern, F major pattern

Theory Review

Notes, rests and time signatures

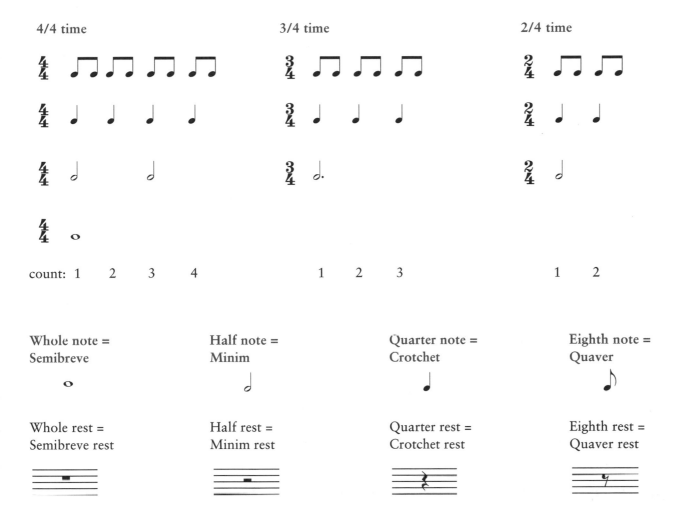

4/4 time   3/4 time   2/4 time

count: 1   2   3   4   1   2   3   1   2

Whole note =   Half note =   Quarter note =   Eighth note =
Semibreve   Minim   Crotchet   Quaver

Whole rest =   Half rest =   Quarter rest =   Eighth rest =
Semibreve rest   Minim rest   Crotchet rest   Quaver rest

Piano notation, key notes and C note positions

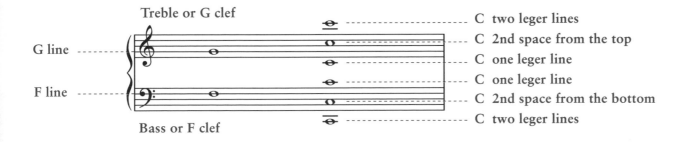

Treble or G clef .... C two leger lines
G line .... C 2nd space from the top
.... C one leger line
.... C one leger line
F line .... C 2nd space from the bottom
Bass or F clef .... C two leger lines

Dynamics (volume)

pianissimo	*pp*	very quiet
piano	*p*	quiet
mezzo piano	*mp*	moderately quiet
mezzo forte	*mf*	moderately loud
forte	*f*	loud
fortissimo	*ff*	very loud
crescendo (cresc.)		gradually getting louder
decrescendo (decresc.)		gradually getting softer
accent	>	emphasized

Tempo

largo	very slow, stately
andante	walking pace, calmly
moderato	at a moderate speed
allegretto	moderately fast
allegro	fast
presto	very fast
ritardando (rit.)	gradually getting slower

Accidentals

♯ = raise (sharp)   ♭ = lower (flat)   ♮ = natural

The Construction of the Major 5-Note Pattern:

Whole Step	Whole Step	Half Step	Whole Step
W	W	H	W

The Construction of the Minor 5-Note Pattern:

Whole Step	Half Step	Whole Step	Whole Step
W	H	W	W

Intervals (distance from one note to another)

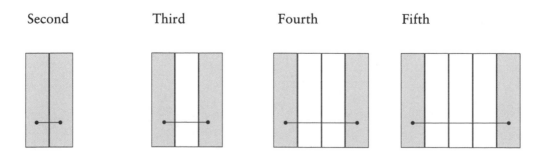

Second   Third   Fourth   Fifth

Glossary

Accent .... > .... Accent sign indicates an emphasis

Allegretto .... Moderately fast

Allegro .... Fast

Andante .... At a walking pace

Articulation .... The joining and separation of notes

Bass clef .... 𝄢 .... Also called the F clef. Notes in the bass clef are usually played with the left hand.

Bourrée .... The Bourrée was originally a French folk dance, which became a courtly dance around 1560 and was popular until well into the 18th century.

Chord .... A set of notes of different pitches sounded together.

Contrary motion .... The parts move in opposite directions.

crescendo .... ◁ .... Gradually getting louder

Curved bracket (Brace, Accolade) .... } ...... This style of bracket is used to join the two staves of the piano system.

Da Capo al Fine...... **D. C. al Fine** .... Play from the beginning until the word *Fine* (end).

decrescendo ..... ▷ .... Gradually getting softer

dolce .... Tenderly, sweetly

Dotted half note / minim ... 𝅗𝅥. .... A dotted half note/minim lasts for three beats as the dot after a note lengthens it by half as much again. It has a clear note head followed by a dot, and has a stem.

Dotted quarter note / crotchet 𝅘𝅥. .... A dotted quarter note/crotchet lasts for one and a half beats as the dot after a note lengthens it by half as much again.

Eighth note / Quaver ...... 𝅘𝅥𝅮 .... A(n) eighth note/quaver has a filled-in note head with a stem and a flag. Two eighth notes equal the value of a quarter note.

Fermata (Pause) .... 𝄐 .... Hold the note on a little longer.

Fifth .... Distance of five notes

Final bar-line .... 𝄂 .... At the end of a piece of music there is a normal bar-line followed by a final thick bar-line.

Flat sign .... ♭ .... A flat sign preceding a note lowers it by a semitone/half step.

Four-four time .... 𝄴 .... Four beats per measure (bar); the quarter note forms the beat.

forte	*f*	Loud
fortissimo	*ff*	Very loud
Fourth		Distance of four notes
Half note / Minim	♩	A half note/minim last for two beats. It has a clear note head with a stem.
Half rest / Minim rest	▬	A half rest/minim rest lasts for two beats.
Improvisation		Make up/invent
Keyboard		The entire collection of piano keys – usually 88
Largo		Very slow, steady, stately
Lateral motion		One part in either hand is held, while the other part moves upwards or downwards.
legato	⌒ ⌣	Play smoothly, without gaps between the notes
Maestoso		Majestically, dignified
Metronome		A device that indicates the beat, helping to control the tempo of a piece.
mezzo forte	*mf*	Moderately loud
mezzo piano	*mp*	Moderately soft
Minuet		The minuet was the most popular courtly dance in the 17th and 18th centuries. It is a partner dance in a moderately fast 3/4 – time, characterised by small steps, intricate patterns and bows.
Moderato		Moderately fast
Natural sign	♮	A natural sign cancels a flat or a sharp from a preceding note. Play the original white key again.
Octave transposition sign	8⌐ 8va⌐	Play the note or notes above which this sign appears, an octave (= 8 notes) higher than written.
Opus	*Op.*	Work, composition
Parallel motion		The parts move in the same direction
Phrase		A musical phrase is often indicated by a curved line or phrase mark.
pianissimo	*pp*	Very quiet
piano	*p*	Soft
poco moto		With a little movement
Presto		Very fast

Quarter note/Crotchet	♩	A quarter note lasts for one beat. It has a filled-in note head with a stem.
Quarter rest/Crotchet rest	𝄽	A quarter note rest lasts for one beat.
Repeat sign	:‖	Play again from the beginning, or repeat the section between two repeat signs.
Repetition		Movement on the same key.
ritardando	*rit.* or *ritard.*	Gradually getting slower
Second		Distance of two notes
Semitone step		A semitone step/half step on the piano is the distance from one key to the next.
Sharp sign	♯	A sharp sign preceding a note raises it by a semitone/half step.
Simile	*sim.*	Similar, continue in the same way
Skip		Movement from one key to the next but one.
staccato	*stacc.* ♩	Short, detached
Step		Movement from one key to the next – upwards or downwards.
Ternary form		This is an A-B-A form, that is, theme A is introduced, followed by a contrasting B theme, returning finally to the A theme.
Third		Distance of three notes
Three-four time	𝟑/𝟒	Three beats per measure (bar); the quarter note forms the beat.
Tie	♩. ‿ ♩.	A tie joins two notes of the same pitch. The tied note is not struck again, but held for the full combined duration.
Transposition		Moving a piece of music into another key.
Treble clef	𝄞	Also called the G clef. Notes in the treble clef are usually played with the right hand.
Two-four time	𝟐/𝟒	Two beats per measure (bar); the quarter note forms the beat.
Upbeat (Anacrusis)		An upbeat or anacrusis is an incomplete bar at the beginning of a piece of music. Together with the final bar of the piece, it usually makes up a complete bar.
Whole note/Semibreve	𝅝	A whole note/semibreve has a clear note head without a stem and lasts for four beats.
Whole rest/Semibreve rest	▬	A whole rest/semibreve rest always corresponds to the duration of a complete bar.

Further Repertoire RC/DC/FF ▶

You can supplement the following lessons of **The Classical Piano Method** with material from the accompanying volumes: **Repertoire Collection 1 (ED 13355)**, **Duet Collection 1 (ED 13439)** and **Finger Fitness 1 (ED 13551)**.

LESSON 5

Repertoire Collection 1: Merry and Sad (H.-G. Heumann)
Wild Horseman (K. G. Hering)
Passion (H.-G. Heumann)

Duet Collection 1: Melody No. 3 (F. Le Couppey)
Melody No. 4 (F. Le Couppey)
In the Light of the Moon (J.-B. Lully)
Long, Long Ago (T. H. Bayly)
Aura Lee (American Folk Song)

Finger Fitness 1: Repetition (H.-G. Heumann)
Steps/Two-Finger Legato (H.-G. Heumann)
Steps/Three-Finger Legato (H.-G. Heumann)
Steps/Four-Finger Legato (H.-G. Heumann)
Steps/Five-Finger Legato (H.-G. Heumann)

LESSON 6

Duet Collection 1: Big Ben (Melody from England)
O sole mio (E. di Capua)
Careless Love (Traditional)

Finger Fitness 1: Two Notes Joined with a Slur (H.-G. Heumann)
Skips (H.-G. Heumann)
Alternating Hands/Tied Notes (H.-G. Heumann)

LESSON 9

Repertoire Collection 1: Melody No. 12 (F. Le Couppey)
March (J. Küffner)
Duet Collection 1: The Beginner Op. 211, No. 1 (C. Gurlitt)
Finger Fitness 1: Playing with Hands Together/ Contrary Motion (H.-G. Heumann)

Finger Fitness 1: Preparatory Legato/Staccato Exercise (H.-G. Heumann)
Exercise with Legato and Staccato (H.-G. Heumann)
Parallel/Contrary/Lateral Motion (H.-G. Heumann)
Sharps and Flats (H.-G. Heumann)
Chromatic Study (H.-G. Heumann)

LESSON 10

Repertoire Collection 1: Hansel and Gretel (German Folk Song)
Lullaby (Melody from Salzburg)
Rock Fever (H.-G. Heumann)
Oragnia figata fa (W. A. Mozart)
Minuet (L. Mozart)
For He's a Jolly Good Fellow (French Folk Tune)

Perfect Day (H.-G. Heumann)
Banks of the Ohio (American Folk Song)

Finger Fitness 1: Quarter Notes (Crotchets) and Eighth Notes (Quavers) (H.-G. Heumann)
Melodic Etude for Five Fingers (H.-G. Heumann)

Duet Collection 1: The Musical Children's Friend Op. 87, No. 1 (H. Wohlfahrt)

Emperor Waltz (J. Strauss, Jr.)

Cuckoo, Cuckoo! (Melody from Austria)

Romance (W. A. Mozart)

Lullaby (J. Brahms)

Horn Concerto No. 2 (W. A. Mozart)

Piano Star (H.-G. Heumann)

LESSON 11

Repertoire Collection 1: The Little Pianist Op. 823, No. 6 (C. Czerny)

Morning Greeting (C. Gurlitt)

Little Melodic Exercise for Beginners Op. 187, No. 13 (C. Gurlitt)

Lullaby (C. Gurlitt)

Finger Fitness 1: Playing in Unison (H.-G. Heumann)

Playing in Contrary Motion (H.-G. Heumann)

Playing in Lateral Motion (H.-G. Heumann)

Little Melodic Study (H.-G. Heumann)

Finger Strength and Equalisation of all Fingers (F. Le Couppey)

LESSON 12

Repertoire Collection 1: Buzz, Buzz, Buzz! (From the Czech Republic)

When the Saints Go Marchin' In (Traditional)

Dance at the Royal Court (H.-G. Heumann)

Beethoven Goes Rock (H.-G. Heumann)

Rule Britannia (T. Arne)

Trumpet Voluntary (J. Clarke)

Radetzky March (J. Strauss, Sr.)

Melody No. 15 (F. Le Couppey)

Presto (D. G. Türk)

Allegro (D. G. Türk)

That Sound is so Lovely (W. A. Mozart)

Antique Dance (J. van den Hove)

Piano Piece Op. 101, No. 39 (F. Beyer)

Duet Collection 1: Russian Dance (P. I. Tchaikovsky)

Finger Fitness 1: Intervals from a Second to a Fifth (H.-G. Heumann)

Right and Left Hand Melody (H.-G. Heumann)

Evenness of all Fingers (H.-G. Heumann)

The Little Pianist Op. 823, No.13 (C. Czerny)

Imitation Study (H.-G. Heumann)

RC / DC / FF ▶ = Repertoire Collection / Duet Collection / Finger Fitness

LESSON 13

Repertoire Collection 1: Andante grazioso W. A. Mozart)

The Little Pianist Op. 823, No. 15 (C. Czerny)

Melody (F. Baumfelder)

Piano Piece Op. 101, No. 61 (F. Beyer)

Fairytale Melody (German Folk Tune)

The Brave Boy (C. Gurlitt)

Minuet (J. Hook)

Gavotte (J. Hook)

Waltz (P. I. Tchaikovsky)

Capriccio Italien (P. I. Tchaikovsky)

Duet Collection 1: Morning Has Broken (Old Gaelic Melody)

The Trout (F. Schubert)

The Elephant (C. Saint-Saëns)

The Musical Children's Friend Op. 87, No. 4 (H. Wohlfahrt)

The Beginner Op. 211, No. 3 (C. Gurlitt)

Finger Fitness 1: TriadExercise (H.-G. Heumann)

Easy Exercise Op.139, No.3 (C. Czerny)

Walking Fingers (H.-G. Heumann)

Ostinato Study (H.-G. Heumann)

Finger Strength and Equalisation of all Fingers: 2 (F. Le Couppey)

The Young Pianist's First Steps Op.82, No.27 (C. Gurlitt)

Evenness and Articulation Study: 1 (H.-G. Heumann)

Accuracy (H.-G. Heumann)

Broken Chord Exercise (H.-G. Heumann)

Preparatory Exercise for No.37 (H.-G. Heumann)

Evenness and Articulation Study: 2 (H.-G. Heumann)

LESSON 14

Repertoire Collection 1: Piano Piece Op. 101, No. 60 (F. Beyer)

Lost in Thought (H.-G. Heumann)

Harlequin (H.-G. Heumann)

Rocky Keys (H.-G. Heumann)

Duet Collection 1: Play in the Morning (D. G. Türk)

Melody No. 5 (F. Le Couppey)

Andante Op. 44, No. 1 (J. A. André)

The Musical Children's Friend Op. 87, No. 15 (H. Wohlfahrt)

Finger Fitness 1: First Instructor Op.599, No.3 (C. Czerny)

BordunExercise (H.-G. Heumann)

Finger Strength Study: 1 (H.-G. Heumann)

Sustaining Fingers (H.-G. Heumann)

Preparatory Exercise for No.43 (H.-G. Heumann)

Finger Strength Study: 2 (H.-G. Heumann)

Rhythmic Articulation Exercise (H.-G. Heumann)

Cross Hand Etude (H.-G. Heumann)

Changes between Two Neighbouring Keys (H.-G. Heumann)

Evenness Study/Alternating Hands (H.-G. Heumann)

LESSON 15

Repertoire Collection 1: Piano My Love (H.-G. Heumann)

Finger Fitness 1: Block Chords and Broken Chords/ The Right-Pedal (H.-G. Heumann)

Skips with Block Chords (H.-G. Heumann)

Skips with Broken Chords (H.-G.Heumann)

Track List

1	Take Two	**37**	Turkish March (accomp.)
2	Take Two (accompaniment)	**38**	Minuet
3	Improvising on the Black Keys (accomp.)	**39**	Presto
4	Piano Dreams	**40**	Prelude
5	Piano Dreams (accomp.)	**41**	Finger Fitness 5
6	Black and White	**42**	Musette
7	Black and White (accomp.)	**43**	Spring
8	Morning in the Countryside	**44**	Finger Fitness 6
9	Morning in the Countryside (accomp.)	**45**	Scherzo
10	Take Five Fingers	**46**	Finger Fitness 7
11	Take Five Fingers (accomp.)	**47**	Ode to Joy
12	Wedding March	**48**	Finger Fitness 8
13	Wedding March (accomp.)	**49**	Air
14	A Little Night Music	**50**	Finger Fitness 9
15	A Little Night Music (accomp.)	**51**	Trumpet Tune
16	Pastoral Song	**52**	Finger Fitness 10
17	Pastoral Song (accomp.)	**53**	For Nannerl
18	Finger Fitness 1	**54**	Largo
19	Finger Fitness 1 (accomp.)	**55**	La Marmotte
20	Twinkle, Twinkle, Little Star!	**56**	Sentimental Dialogue
21	Twinkle, Twinkle, Little Star! (accomp.)	**57**	Finger Fitness 11
22	Finger Fitness 2	**58**	Bourrée
23	Finger Fitness 2 (accomp.)	**59**	Symphony No.1
24	Cancan	**60**	Dance of the Little Swans
25	Cancan (accomp.)	**61**	Finger Fitness 12
26	Surprise Symphony	**62**	Symphony No.7
27	Surprise Symphony (accomp.)	**63**	Sound Painting
28	Finger Fitness 3	**64**	Longing For You
29	Finger Fitness 3 (accomp.)	**65**	Dream of Love
30	Longing for Spring		
31	Longing for Spring (accomp.)		
32	Finger Fitness 4		
33	Barcarolle		
34	Barcarolle (accomp.)		
35	Discovery Waltz		
36	Turkish March		

Recording Acknowledgments

Recorded October 2011
Piano - Samantha Ward, Maciej Raginia
Engineered and Mixed by Ken Blair, BMP recording
Produced by Ateş Orga

Audio files can be downloaded for free with the following voucher code on
www.schott-music.com/online-material: VwjwZSu5

Keyboard Notation System

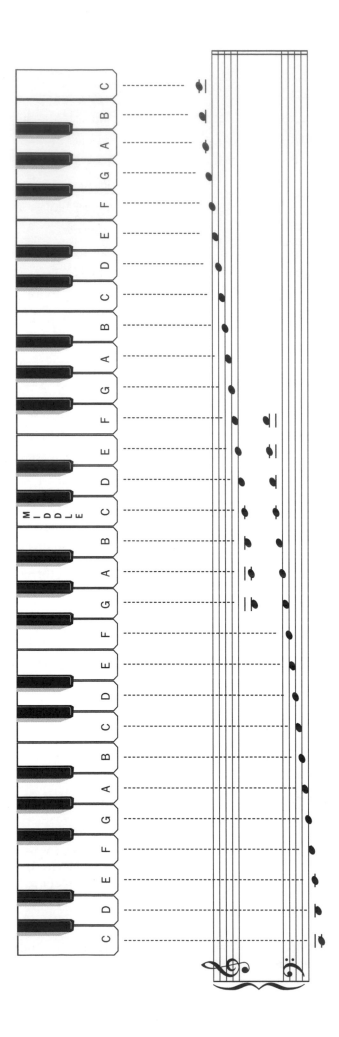

ŠEVČÍK

OPUS 3

40 VARIATIONS/
VARIATIONEN

FOR
CELLO

ARR. FEUILLARD

BOSWORTH

40 Variationen
von O. Ševčík Op.3
für Violoncello übertragen von
L. R. FEUILLARD.

40 Variations
de O. Ševčík Op.3
transcrites pour Violoncelle par
L. R. FEUILLARD.

40 variací
od O. Ševčíka op.3
pro violoncello upravil
L. R. FEUILLARD.

40 Variations
O. Ševčík Op.3
transcribed for Violoncello by
L. R. FEUILLARD.

40 варіацій.
Сост. О. О. Шевчикъ. Op. 3
Для віолончели переложилъ
L. R. FEUILLARD.

ABKÜRZUNGEN UND ZEICHEN:

G.	Ganzer Bogen.
H.	Halber Bogen.
u.H.	Untere Hälfte.
o.H.	Obere Hälfte.
Fr.	Am Frosch des Bogens.
M.	Mitte des Bogens.
Sp.	Spitze des Bogens.
⊓	Herunterstrich.
V	Hinaufstrich.
—	Breit stossen.
•	Abgestossen oder gehämmert.
ꞌ	Geworfen (spiccato) oder springend.
)	Bogen heben.

ABREVIATIONS ET SIGNES:

G.	*Tout l'archet.*
H.	*Moitié d'archet.*
u.H.	*Moitié infériere.*
o.H.	*Moitié supériere.*
Fr.	*Talon de l'archet.*
M.	*Milieu de l'archet.*
Sp.	*Pointe de l'archet.*
⊓	*Tirez.*
V	*Poussez.*
—	*Détaché large.*
•	*Staccato ou martelé.*
ꞌ	*Jeté (spiccato) ou sautillé.*
)	*Lever l'archet.*

ABBREVIATIONS AND SIGNS:

G.	Whole bow-length.
H.	Half bow-length.
u.H.	Lower half bow-length.
o.H.	Upper half bow-length.
Fr.	Frog (nut, or heel) of the bow.
M.	Bow-middle.
Sp.	Tip of the bow.
⊓	Down-stroke.
V	Up-stroke.
—	Broad (detached) staccato.
•	Hammered staccato (martellato).
ꞌ	Jerked (ricochet) or hopping staccato.
)	Raise the bow.

ZKRATKY A ZNAMENÍ.

G.	*celým smyccem.*
H.	*polovičním smyccem.*
u.H.	*dolejší polovicí.*
o.H.	*hořejší polovicí.*
Fr.	*U žabky smýčce.*
M.	*Středem smýčce.*
Sp.	*Hrotem smýčce.*
⊓	*smyk dolů.*
V	*smyk nahoru.*
—	*širokým tahem.*
•	*odráženě aneb potepem.*
ꞌ	*Úderem (spiccato) aneb poskokem.*
)	*zdvih smýčce.*

СОКРАЩЕНІЯ И ЗНАКИ:

G.	Цѣлымъ смычкомъ.
H.	Половиною смычка.
u.H.	Нижнею половиною.
o.H.	Верхнею половиною.
Fr.	У колодочки.
M.	Серединою смычка.
Sp.	Концомъ смычка.
⊓	Смычкомъ внизъ.
V	Смычкомъ вверхъ.
—	Протяжнымъ штрихомъ.
•	Отрывисто.
ꞌ	Отскакивающимъ или прыгающимъ смычкомъ.
)	Снять смычокъ.

Edited and translated by H. Brett. *Edited by L. R. Feuillard and A. E. Bosworth.*

Var.11. Allegro. ♩=152.

Var.12. Allegro. ♩=84.

Var.13. Allegro. ♩=152.

VERÄNDERUNGEN DES BOGENSTRICHES. CHANGEMENTS DE COUPS D'ARCHET. CHANGES OF BOWING-STYLES.

ZMĚNY SMYKU. ПЕРЕМѢНЫ ДВИЖЕНІЙ СМЫЧКА.

A) B)

8

14

VERÄNDERUNGEN DES BOGENSTRICHES.   CHANGEMENTS DE COUPS D'ARCHET.   CHANGES OF BOWING-STYLES.
ZMĚNY SMYKŮ.   ПЕРЕМѢНЫ ДВИЖЕНІЙ СМЫЧКА.

VERÄNDERUNGEN DES BOGENSTRICHES.   CHANGEMENTS DE COUPS D'ARCHET.   CHANGES OF BOWING-STYLES.

ZMĚNY SMYKŮ.   ПЕРЕМѢНЫ ДВИЖЕНІИ СМЫЧКА.

B. & Cọ 6157

VERÄNDERUNGEN DER ARPEGGIEN. CHANGEMENTS DES ARPEGES. CHANGES OF THE ARPEGGIOS.
ZMĚNY V ARPEZIÍCH. ПЕРЕМѢНЫ АРПЕДЖІЙ.